Technical interview Questions and Answers : Electrical **Engineering**

Manjiri Pravin Sutar - Kulkarni
Gopal Ramchandra Kulkarni

Technical interview Questions with Answers : Electrical Engineering

Collection of 450 Questions with Answers

LAP LAMBERT Academic Publishing

Cover image: www.ingimage.com

Publisher:
LAP LAMBERT Academic Publishing
is a trademark of
International Book Market Service Ltd., member of OmniScriptum Publishing Group
17 Meldrum Street, Beau Bassin 71504, Mauritius
Printed at: see last page
ISBN: 978-620-2-56413-7

INDEX

Technical interview Questions with Answers:

Electrical Engineering

…..Collection of 450 Questions with Answers

BY

➢ Er.Manjiri Pravin Sutar-Kulkarni , M.Tech.(Electrical Engg), is having Industrial Experience of 7+ years. Presently associated with Konecranes India Private Limited, Pune 411006 , India

➢ DR.G. R. Kulkarni, Ph.D. (C.S.E.), is having 34 years of experience in Engineering Education Field. Presently associated with ADCET-Ashta 416301 India

Interview preparation session - 1

1.   What happens if we connect a capacitor to a generator load?

Connecting a capacitor across a generator always improves power factor, but it will help depends up on the engine capacity of the alternator, otherwise the alternator will be over loaded due to the extra watts consumed due to the improvement on pf. Secondly, don't connect a capacitor across an alternator while it is picking up or without any other load.

2.   Why the capacitors works on ac only?

Generally capacitor gives infinite resistance to dc components (i.e., block the DC components). It allows the ac components to pass through.

3.   Explain the working principal of the circuit breaker?

Circuit Breaker is one which makes or breaks the circuit. It has two contacts namely fixed contact & moving contact. Under normal condition the moving contact comes in contact with fixed contact thereby forming the closed contact for the flow of current. During abnormal & faulty conditions (when current exceeds the rated value) an arc is produced between the fixed & moving contacts & thereby it forms the open circuit, Arc is extinguished by the Arc Quenching media like air, oil, vacuum etc.

4.   How many types of colling system it transformers?

1. ONAN (oil natural, air natural)
2. ONAF (oil natural, air forced)
3. OFAF (oil forced, air forced)
4. ODWF (oil direct, water forced)
5. OFAN (oil forced, air forced)

5.   What is the function of anti-pumping in circuit breaker?

when breaker is close at one time by close push button, the anti-pumping contactor prevent re close the breaker by close push button after if it already close.

6. What is stepper motor? What is its uses?

Stepper motor is the electrical machine which act upon input pulse applied to it.it is one type of synchronous motor which runs in steps in either direction instead of running in complete cycle.so, in automation parts it is used.

7. Tell me in detail about c.t. and p.t.?

The term C.T means current transformer, and the term P.T means potential transformer. In circuit where measurements of high voltage and high current is involved, they are used there. Particularly when a measuring device like voltmeter or ammeter is not able to measure such high value of quantity because of large value of torque due to such high value it can damage the measuring device. so, CT and PT are introduced in the circuits. They work on the same principle of transformer, which is based on linkage of electromagnetic flux produced by primary with secondary. They work on the ratio to they are designed. E.g. if CT is of ratio 5000\5A and it has to measure secondary current of 8000A.then ANS=8000*5\5000=8Aand this result will be given to ammeter .and after measuring 8A we can calculate the primary current. Same is the operation of PT but measuring voltage.

8. There are a Transformer and an induction machine. Those two have the same supply. For which device the load current will be maximum? And why?

The motor has max load current compare to that of transformer because the motor consumes real power and the transformer is only producing the working flux and it's not consuming. Hence the load current in the transformer is because of core loss so it is minimum.

9. What is power factor? Whether it should be high or low? Why?

Power factor should be high in order to get smooth operation of the system. Low power factor means losses will be more.it is the ratio of true power to apparent power. It has to be ideally 1. If it is too low then cable over heating &equipment overloading will occur. If it is

5

greater than 1 then load will act as capacitor and starts feeding the source and will cause tripping. (If pf is poor ex: 0.17 to meet actual power load has to draw more current (V constant), result in more losses if pf is good ex: 0.95 to meet actual power load has to draw less current (V constant), result in less losses)

10.   What is the difference between Isolator and Circuit Breaker?

Isolator is an off load device which is used for isolating the downstream circuits from upstream circuits for the reason of any maintenance on downstream circuits. It is manually operated and does not contain any solenoid unlike circuit breaker. It should not be operated while it is having load. First the load on it must be made zero and then it can safely operate. Its specification only rated current is given. But circuit breaker is on load automatic device used for breaking the circuit in case of abnormal conditions like short circuit, overload etc., it is having three specification 1 is rated current and 2 is short circuit breaking capacity and 3 is instantaneous tripping current .

11.   What is Boucholz relay and the significance of it in to the transformer?

Boucholz relay is a device which is used for the protection of transformer from its internal faults, it is a gas based relay. whenever any internal fault occurs in a transformer, the Boucholz relay at once gives a horn for some time, if the transformer is isolated from the circuit then it stop its sound itself otherwise it trips the circuit by its own tripping mechanism.

12.   What is SF6 Circuit Breaker?

SF6 is Sulphur hexa Fluoride gas. If this gas is used as arc quenching medium in a Circuit breaker means SF6 CB

13.   What is ferrantic effect?

Output voltage is greater than the input voltage or receiving end voltage is greater than the sending end voltage.

14.   What is meant by insulation voltage in cables? Explain it?

It is the property of a cable by virtue of it can withstand the applied voltage without rupturing it is known as insulation level of the cable.

15. Why we do 2 types of earthing on transformer (i.e. :) body earthing & neutral earthing, what is function. i am going to install a 5oo kva transformer & 380 kva DG set what should the earthing value?

The two types of earthing are Familiar as Equipment earthing and system earthing. In Equipment earthing: body (non-conducting part) of the equipment should be earthed to safeguard the human beings. System Earthing: In this neutral of the supply source (Transformer or Generator) should be grounded. With this, in case of unbalanced loading neutral will not be shifted.so that unbalanced voltages will not arise. We can protect the equipment also. With size of the equipment (transformer or alternator) and selection of relying system earthing will be further classified into directly earthed, Impedance earthing, resistive (NGRs) earthing.

16. What is the difference between MCB & MCCB, Where it can be used?

MCB is miniature circuit breaker which is thermal operated and use for short circuit protection in small current rating circuit. MCCB moulded case circuit breaker and is thermal operated for over load current and magnetic operation for instant trip in short- circuit condition. Under voltage and under frequency may be inbuilt. Normally it is used where normal current is more than 100A

17. What is use of lockout relay in ht voltage?

A lock-out relay is generally placed in line before or after the e-stop switch so the power can be shut off at one central location. This relay is powered by the same electrical source as the control power and is operated by a key lock switch. The relay itself may have up to 24 contact points within the unit itself. This allows the control power for multiple machines to be locked out by the turn of a single key switch.

18. What is the difference between earth resistance and earth electrode resistance?

Only one of the terminals is evident in the earth resistance. In order to find the second terminal we should recourse to its definition: Earth Resistance is the resistance existing between the electrically accessible part of a buried electrode and another point of the earth, which is far away. The resistance of the electrode has the following components :(A) The resistance of the metal and that of the connection to it. (B) The contact resistance of the surrounding earth to the electrode

.

19. Which power plant has high load factor?

All base load power plants have a high load factor. If we use high efficiency power plants to supply the base load, we can reduce the cost of generation. Hydro power plants have a higher efficiency than thermal & nuclear power plants.

20. Why an ac solenoid valve attract the plunger even though we interchanges the terminal? Will the poles changes?

Yes because the poles changes for every half-cycle of ac voltage so the polarity of AC voltage is continuously changing for every half cycle. So, interchanging of terminals in ac system does not show any difference. That's why the ac solenoid attract the plunger even though it's terminals are interchanged.

21. Define IDMT relay?

It is an inverse definite minimum time relay. In IDMT relay its operating is inversely proportional and also a characteristic of minimum time after which this relay operates. It is inverse in the sense, the tripping time will decrease as the magnitude of fault current increase.

22. What are the transformer losses?

TRANSFORMER LOSSES - Transformer losses have two sources-copper loss and magnetic loss. Copper losses are caused by the resistance of the wire (I2R).Magnetic losses are caused by eddy currents and hysteresis in the core. Copper loss is a constant after the coil has been wound and therefore a measurable loss. Hysteresis is loss is constant for a particular voltage and current. Eddy-current loss, however, is different for each frequency passed through the transformer.

23. What is meant by regenerative braking?

When the supply is cut off for a running motor, it still continue running due to inertia. In order to stop it quickly we place a load (resistor) across the armature winding and the motor should have maintained continuous field supply. So that back emf voltage is made to apply across the resistor and due to load the motor stops quickly. This type of breaking is called as "Regenerative Breaking".

24. Why is the starting current high in a DC motor?

In DC motors, Voltage equation is $V=E_b-I_aR_a$ (V = Terminal voltage, E_b = Back emf in Motor, I_a = Armature current, R_a = Armature resistance).At starting, E_b is zero. Therefore, $V=I_aR_a$, I_a = V/R_a, where R_a is very less like 0.01ohm.i.e, I_a will become enormously increased.

25. What are the advantages of star-delta starter with induction motor?

(1). The main advantage of using the star delta starter is reduction of current during the starting of the motor. Starting current is reduced to 3-4 times Of current of Direct online starting.
(2). Hence the starting current is reduced , the voltage drops during the starting of motor in systems are reduced.

26. Why Delta Star Transformers are used for Lighting Loads?

For lighting loads, neutral conductor is must and hence the secondary must be star winding and this lighting load is always unbalanced in all three phases. To minimize the current unbalance in the primary we use delta winding in the primary. So delta / star transformer is used for lighting loads.

27. Why in a three pin plug the earth pin is thicker and longer than the other pins?

It depends upon R=rho l/a where area(a) is inversely proportional to resistance(R), so if (a) increases, R decreases & if R is less the leakage current will take low resistance path so the earth pin should be thicker. It is longer because the First to make the connection and last to disconnect should be earth Pin. This assures Safety for the person who uses the electrical instrument.

28. Why series motor cannot be started on no-load?

Series motor cannot be started without load because of high starting torque. Series motor are used in Trains, Crane etc.

29. Why ELCB can't work if N input of ELCB do not connect to ground?

ELCB is used to detect earth leakage fault. Once the phase and neutral are connected in an ELCB, the current will flow through phase and that much current will have to return neutral so resultant current is zero. Once there is a ground fault in the load side, current from phase will directly pass through earth and it will not return through neutral through ELCB. That means once side current is going and not returning and hence because of this difference in current ELCB will trip and it will safe guard the other circuits from faulty loads. If the neutral is not grounded, fault current will definitely high and that full fault current will come back through ELCB, and there will be no difference in current.

30. How electrical power is generated by an A.C Generator?

For the generation of elect power we need a prime mover which supplies mechanical power input to the alternator, can be steam turbines, or hydro turbines. When poles of the rotor moves under the armature conductors which are placed on the stator ,field flux cut the armature conductor ,therefore voltage is generated and is of sinusoidal in nature...due to polarity change of rotor poles(i,e) N-S-N-S.

31. Why an ac solenoid valve attract the plunger even though we interchanges the terminal? Will the poles changes?

Yes because the poles changes for every half-cycle of ac voltage so the polarity of AC voltage is continuously changing for every half cycle. So, interchanging of terminals in ac system does not show any difference. That's why the ac solenoid attract the plunger even though its terminals are interchanged.

AVR is an abbreviation for Automatic Voltage Regulator. It is important part in Synchronous Generators, it controls the output voltage of the generator by controlling its excitation current. Thus it can control the output Reactive Power of the Generator.

32. What is an exciter and how does it work

There are two types of exciters, static exciter and rotary exciter. Purpose of exciter is to supply the excitation dc voltage to the fixed poles of generator. Rotary exciter is an additional small generator mounted on the shaft of main generator. If it is dc generator, it will supply dc to the rotary poles through slip ring and brushes (conventional alternator). if it is an ac exciter, output of ac exciter is rectified by rotating diodes and supply dc to main fixed poles.ac exciter is the ac generator whose field winding are stationary and armature rotates. Initial voltage is built up by residual magnetism. It gives the starting torque to the generator.

33. Difference between a four point starter and three point starter?

The shunt connection in four point stater is provided separately from the line where as in three point stater it is connected with line which is the drawback in three point stater

34. Why use the VCB at High Transmission System? Why can't use ACB?

Actually the thing is vacuum has high arc quenching property compare to air because in VCB, the die electric strengths equal to 8 times of air. That y always vacuum used as in HT breaker and air used as in LT.

35. What is the difference between surge arrestor and lightning arrestor?

LA is installed outside and the effect of lightning is grounded, whereas surge arrestor installed inside panels comprising of resistors which consumes the energy and nullify the effect of surge.

36. Why syn. generators r used for the production of electricity?

synchronous machines have capability to work on different power factor (or say different imaginary POW varying the field emf. Hence syn. generators r used for the production of electricity.

37. Enlist types of dc generator?

D.C. Generators are classified into two types
1) Separately excited d.c.generator
2) Self-excited d.c.generator, which is further classified into; 1) series 2) shunt and
3) Compound (which is further classified into cumulative and differential).

38. What is the difference between synchronous generator & asynchronous generator?

In simple, synchronous generator supply's both active and reactive power but asynchronous generator (induction generator) supply's only active power and observe reactive power for magnetizing. This type of generators are used in windmills.

39. Give two basic speed control scheme of DC shunt motor?

1. By using flux control method: in this method a rheostat is connected across the field winding to control the field current.so by changing the current the flux produced by the field winding can be changed, and since speed is inversely proportional to flux speed can be controlled
2. Armature control method: in this method a rheostat is connected across armature winding by varying the resistance the value of resistive drop (IaRa) can be varied, and since speed is directly proportional to Eb-IaRa the speed can be controlled.

40. What is the principle of motor?

Whenever a current carrying conductor is placed in a magnetic field it produce turning or twisting movement is called as torque.

41. What is meant by armature reaction?

The effect of armature flu to main flux is called armature reaction. The armature flux may support main flux or opposes main flux.

42. What is the Polarization index value? (Pi value) and simple definition of polarization index?

Its ratio between insulation resistance (IR) i.e. meggar value for 10min to insulation resistance for 1 min. It ranges from 5-7 for new motors & normally for motor to be in good condition it should be Greater than 2.5.

Polarization Index Test (PI) – The PI test measures the ability of the insulation to absorb voltage over a period of time. This gives an indication of the overall insulation quality of the individual pieces of insulation in the transformer. This test is usually performed in conjunction with the Meggar Test. It is measured as ratio of insulation resistance (IR) for 10 minutes to insulation resistance for 1 minute.

43. What will happen when power factor is leading in distribution of power? If there is high power factor, i.e. if the power factor is close to one:

1. Losses in form of heat will be reduced,
2. Cable becomes less bulky and easy to carry, and very cheap to afford, &
3. It also reduces over heating of transformers.

44. How Many Interrupts Are There In 8085?

There are 12 interrupts in 8085.

45. Advantages of vvvf drives over non vvvf drives for EOT cranes? :

1. Smooth start and stop.
2. No jerking of load.
3. Exact positioning

4. Better protection for motor.

5. high/low speed selection.

6. Reliability of break shoe.

7. Programmable break control.

8. Easy circuitry

9. Reduction in controls

10. Increases motor life

46. What is the significance of vector grouping in Power Transformers?

Every power transformer has a vector group listed by its manufacturer. Fundamentally it tells you the information about how the windings are connected (delta or wye) and the phase difference between the current and voltage. EG. DYN11 means Delta primary, Wye Secondary and the current is at 11 o clock referred to the voltage.

47. Type of A.C motor is used in the fan (ceiling fan, exhaust fan, pedestal fan, bracket fan etc) which are find in the houses?

Its Single Phase induction motor which mostly squirrel cage rotor and are capacitor start capacitor run.

48. Why, when birds sit on transmission lines or current wires doesn't get shock?

It's true that if birds touch the single one line (phase or neutral) they don't get electrical shock… if birds touch 2 lines than the circuit is closed and they get electrical shock. so if a human touch single one line (phase) then he doesn't get shock if he is in the air (not touching – standing on the ground if he is standing on the ground then touching the line (phase) he will get a shock because the ground on what we standing is like line (ground bed – like neutral) I and in the most of electric lines the neutral is grounded. So that means that human who touch the line closes the circuit between phase and neutral.

49. What happens if we give 220 volts dc supply to tube light?

Bulbs [devices] for AC are designed to operate such that it offers high impedance to AC supply. Normally they have low resistance. When DC supply is applied, due to low resistance, the current through lamp would be so high that it may damage the bulb element.

50. Which motor has high Starting Torque and Staring current DC motor, Induction motor or Synchronous motor?

DC Series motor has high starting torque. We cannot start the Induction motor and Synchronous motors on load, but cannot start the DC series motor without load.

51. What is vacuum circuit breaker? Define with cause and where we use it.

A breaker is normally used to break a circuit. While breaking the circuit, the contact terminals will be separated. At the time of separation an air gap is formed in between the terminals. Due to existing current flow the air in the gap is ionized and results in the arc. Various mediums are used to quench this arc in respective CB's. But in VCB the medium is vacuum gas. Since the air in the CB is having vacuum pressure the arc formation is interrupted. VCB's can be used up to 11kv.

52. What is ACSR cable and where we use it?

ACSR means Aluminum conductor steel reinforced, this conductor is used in transmission & distribution

.

53. What's is MARX CIRCUIT?

It is used with generators for charging a number of capacitor in parallel and discharging them in series. It is used when voltage required for testing is higher than the available.

54. What is the principle of motor?

Whenever a current carrying conductor is placed in a magnetic field it produce turning or twisting movement is called as torque.

55. What is electric traction?

Traction means using the electric power for traction system i.e. for railways, trams, trolleys etc. electric traction means use of the electricity for all these. Now a days, magnetic traction is also used for bullet trains. Basically dc motors are used for electric traction systems.

56. How can you start-up the 40w tube lite with 230v AC/DC without using any choke/Coil?

It's possible by means of Electronic choke. Otherwise it's not possible to ionize the particles in tube. Light, with normal voltage. Pu stands for per unit and this will be used in power system single line diagram there it is like a huge electrical circuit with no of components (generators, transformers, loads) with different ratings (in MVA and KV). To bring all the ratings into common platform we use pu concept in which, in general largest MVA and KV ratings of the component is considered as base values, then all other component ratings will get back into this basis. Those values are called as pu values. (p.u=actual value/base value).

57. Operation carried out in Thermal power station?

The water is obtained in the boiler and the coal is burnt so that steam is obtained this steam is allowed to hit the turbine, the turbine which is coupled with the generator generates the electricity.

58. Why link is provided in neutral of an ac circuit and fuse in phase of ac circuit?

Link is provided at a Neutral common point in the circuit from which various connection are taken for the individual control circuit and so it is given in a link form to withstand high Amps. But in the case of Fuse in the Phase of AC circuit it is designed such that the fuse rating is calculated for the particular circuit (i.e. load) only. So if any malfunction happen the fuse connected in the particular control circuit alone will blow off.

59. Enlist types of dc generator?

D.C. Generators are classified into two types 1)separately excited d.c.generator 2)self-excited d.c.generator, which is further classified into;1)series 2)shunt and 3)compound(which is further classified into cumulative and differential).

60. What is the difference between an Electronic regulator and ordinary rheostat regulator for fans?

The difference between the electronic and ordinary regulator is that in electronic reg. power losses are less i.e. for as we decrease the speed the electronic reg. give the power needed for that particular speed but in case of ordinary rh type reg. the power wastage is same for every speed and no power is saved. In electronic regulator triac is employed for speed cntrl.by varying the firing angle speed is controlled but in rheostat ctrl resistance is decreased by steps to achieve speed control.

61. What was the difference between Electrical Engineering and Electronics Engineering?

Electrical engineering is a field of engineering that generally deals with the study and application of electricity, electronics, and electromagnetism. Electronics engineering, or electronic engineering, is an engineering discipline where non-linear and active electrical components such as electron tubes, and semiconductor devices, especially transistors, diodes and integrated circuits, are utilized to design electronic circuits, devices and systems, typically also including passive electrical components and based on printed circuit boards.

62. What is an exciter and how does it work?

There are two types of exciters, static exciter and rotary exciter. Purpose of exciter is to supply the excitation dc voltage to the fixed poles of generator. Rotary exciter is an additional small generator mounted on the shaft of main generator. If it is dc generator, it will supply dc to the rotary poles through slip ring and brushes (conventional alternator). if it is an ac exciter, output of ac exciter is rectified by rotating diodes and supply dc to main fixed poles.ac exciter is the ac generator whose field winding are stationary and armature rotates. Initial voltage is built up by residual magnetism. It gives the starting torque to the generator.

63. Explain the term BOM?

BOM stands for Bill of Materials; it is a list of item or parts that makeup a product assembly. For example, a lawn mower requires a handle assembly, metal deck assembly, a control assembly, motor and blade assembly.

64. Explain what is QMS?

QMS stands for Quality Management System; it documents all necessary information about company's design and operational controls, including issue reporting, monitoring, continuous improvement and training, to make sure that company delivers continuous product.

65.   What is the challenge in manufacturing products?

Main challenge in manufacturing is to develop better production processes, ensure the right material and component supplies at the least cost, decrease production time, eliminate wastage and maintain quality in the final product.

66.   Define the term "factory overhead"?

During the manufacturing process, whatever the cost is incurred during the process is referred as "factory overhead", excluding the cost of materials and direct labors.

67.   Explain how to supervise in a manufacturing unit?

Supervising a manufacturing process includes attending to the individual phases of the production. Also, manufacturing supervisor should have a close eye on the inventory that going to be used.

Step 1: Keep the records of different phases of manufacturing also analyse whether the amount of product produced by the crew is enough to meet the demand

Step 2: Look for the bottlenecks in the unit and see how you can eliminate it

Step 3: Keep the track of inventory and try to reduce the liquid capital used after unused material

Step 4: Examine the final goods to determine whether they meet the company's quality standards

.

68.   Explain the process of commutation in a dc machine. Explain what are inter-poles and why they are required in a dc machine.

Commutation is phenomenon when an armature coil moves under the influence of one pole-pair; it carries constant current in one direction. As the coil moves into the influence of the next pole- pair, the current in it must reverse. This reversal of current in a coil is called commutation. Several coils undergo commutation simultaneously. The reversal of current is opposed by the static coil emf and therefore must be aided in some fashion for smooth current reversal, which otherwise would result in sparking at the brushes. The aiding emf is dynamically induced into the coils undergoing commutation by means of compoles or interpoles, which are series excited by the armature current. These are located in the interpolar region of the main poles and therefore influence the armature coils only when these undergo commutation.

69. Comment on the working principle of operation of a single-phase transformer.

An AC supply passes through the primary winding, a current will start flowing in the primary winding. As a result, the flux is set. This flux is linked with primary and secondary windings. Hence, voltage is induced in both the windings. Now, when the load is connected to the secondary side, the current will start flowing in the load in the secondary winding, resulting in the flow of additional current in the secondary winding. Hence, according to Faraday's laws of electromagnetic induction, emf will be induced in both the windings. The voltage induced in the primary winding is due to its self-inductance and known as self-induced emf and according to Lenses' law it will oppose the cause i.e. supply voltage hence called as back emf. The voltage induced in secondary coil is known as mutually induced voltage. Hence, transformer works on the principle of electromagnetic induction.

70. What is rated speed?

At the time of motor taking normal current (rated current) the speed of the motor is called rated speed. It is a speed at which any system take small current and give maximum efficiency.

71. If one lamp connects between two phases it will glow or not?

If the voltage between the two phases is equal to the lamp voltage then the lamp will glow. When the voltage difference is big it will damage the lamp and when the difference is smaller the lamp will glow depending on the type of lamp.

72. In 8085 Which Is Called As High Order / Low Order Register?

Flag is called as Low order register & Accumulator is called as High order Register.

73. Two bulbs of 100w and 40w respectively connected in series across a 230v supply which bulb will glow bright and why?

Since two bulbs are in series they will get equal amount of electrical current but as the supply voltage is constant across the bulb (P=V^2/R).So the resistance of 40W bulb is greater and voltage across 40W is more (V=IR) so 40W bulb will glow brighter.

74. Why temperature rise is conducted in bus bars and isolators?

Bus bars and isolators are rated for continuous power flow that means they carry heavy currents which rises their temperature. So it is necessary to test this devices for temperature rise.

75. What is a System?

When a number of elements or components are connected in a sequence to perform a specific function, the group of elements that all constitute a System

76. What is Control System?

In a System the output and inputs are interrelated in such a manner that the output quantity or variable is controlled by input quantity, then such a system is called Control System.
The output quantity is called controlled variable or response and the input quantity is called command signal or excitation.

77. What are different types of Control Systems?

Two major types of Control Systems are 1) Open loop Control System 2) Closed Loop Control Systems
Open loop Control Systems: The Open loop Control System is one in which the Output

Quantity has no effect on the Input Quantity. No feedback is present from the output quantity to the input quantity for correction.

Closed Loop Control System: The Closed loop Control System is one in which the feedback is provided from the Output quantity to the input quantity for the correction so as to maintain the desired output of the system.

78. What is a feedback in Control System?

The Feedback in Control System in one in which the output is sampled and proportional signal is fed back to the input for automatic correction of the error (any change in desired output) for further processing to get back the desired output.

79. Why Negative Feedback is preferred in the Control System?

The role of Feedback in control system is to take the sampled output back to the input and compare output signal with input signal for error (deviation from the desired result).

Negative Feedback results in the better stability of the system and rejects any disturbance signals and is less sensitive to the parameter variations. Hence in control systems negative feedback is considered.

80. What is the effect of positive feedback on stability of the system?

Positive feedback is not used generally in the control system because it increases the error signal and drives the system to instability. But positive feedbacks are used in minor loop control systems to amplify certain internal signals and parameters.

81. What is protective relay?

It is an electrical device designed to initiate the isolation of a part of the electrical installation, or to operate an alarm signal, in the event of abnormal condition or a fault. In simple words relay is an electrical device that gives signal to isolation device (eg: Circuit Breaker) after sensing the fault and helps to isolate the fault system from the healthy electrical system

82. What are the different relays that employed for protection of apparatus and transmission lines?

The relays that are usually employed for protection of transmission lines include: Over current relay, Directional relay, Distance relay, Under Voltage relay, Under-frequency relay Thermal relay, Differential relay, Phase sequence relays,pilot relays

83. How the electrical power system protection is divided?

The overall system protection is divided into Generator protection, Transformer protection, Bus bar protection,Transmission line protection and Feeder protection

84. How relays are connected in the power system?

The relays are connected to the power system through the current transformer (CT) or potential transformer (PT).

85. What are different types of principles of operation of electro-mechanical relays?

Eletro-mechanical relays operate by two principles. Electro-magnetic attraction and electro-magnetic induction. In electromagnetic attraction relay plunger is drawn to the solenoid or an armature is attracted to the poles of the electromagnet. In case of electro-magnetic induction, principle of operation is similar to induction motor. Torque is developed by electromagnetic induction principle

86. Action carried out by the relay and circuit breaker during fault condition?

After the relay sensing the fault condition, relay operates and close the trip coils. The effect of this will be circuit breaker operate to open the contacts.

87. What is electric traction?

Electric traction means using the electric power for traction system (i.e. for railways,trams, trolleys etc). Electric traction means use of the electricity for all the above machines. Now a days, magnetic traction is also used for bullet trains. and basically dc motors are used for electric traction systems.

88. How can you start-up the 40w tube light with 230v AC/DC without using any choke/Coil?

It's possible by means of Electronic chokes, otherwise it's not possible to ionize the particles in tube light with normal voltage.

89. Explain Briefly The Flag Register In The 8085 Microprocessor.?
- The flag register in 8085 is an 8-bit register which contains 5 bit positions.
- These five flags are of 1bit F/F and are known as zero, sign, carry, parity and auxiliary carry.
- For sign flag if the result of an MSB operation is 1 then it is set else it is reset.
- The zero flag is set of the result of an instruction is zero.
- The auxiliary carry flag is used for BCD operations, not free to the programmer.
- The carry flag is used for carrying and borrowing in case of addition and subtraction operations.
- The parity flag is used for results containing an even number of one's.

89. Operation carried out in Thermal power stations?

The water is obtained in the boiler and the coal is burnt so that steam is obtained this steam is allowed to hit the turbine , the turbine which is coupled with the generator generates the electricity.

90. Why link is provided in neutral of an ac circuit and fuse in phase of an AC circuit?

Link is provided at a Neutral common point in the circuit from which various connection are taken for the individual control circuit and so it is given in a link form to withstand high Amps. But in the case of Fuse in the Phase of AC circuit it is designed such that the fuse rating is calculated for the particular circuit (i.e load) only.So if any malfunction happen the fuse connected in the particular control circuit alone will blow off.

91. What is the difference between electronic regulator and ordinary electrical rheostat

regulator for fans?

The difference between the electronic and ordinary electrical regulator is that in electronic regulator power losses are less because as we decrease the speed the electronic regulator gives the power needed for that particular speed but in case of ordinary rheostat type regulator, the power wastage is same for every speed and no power is saved.In electronic regulator, triac is employed for speed control by varying the firing angle speed and it is controlled but in rheostatic ,control resistance is decreased by steps to achieve speed control.

92.   How tube light circuit is connected and how it works?

A choke is connected in one end of the tube light and a starter is in series with the circuit. When supply is provided ,the starter will interrupt the supply cycle of AC. Due to the sudden change of supply the chock will generate around 1000volts . his volt will capable of to break the electrons inside the tube to make electron flow. once the current passes through the tube the starter circuit will be out of part. now there is no change of supply causes choke voltage normalized and act as minimize the current.

93.   what is MARX CIRCUIT?

It is used with generators for charging a number of capacitor in parallel and discharging them in series.It is used when voltage required for testing is higher than the available.

94.   What is encoder, how it function?

An encoder is a device used to change a signal (such as a bitstream) or data into a code. The code may   serve any of a number of purposes such as compressing information for transmission or storage, encrypting or adding redundancies to the input code, or translating from one code to another. This is usually done by means of a programmed algorithm, especially if any part is digital, while most analog encoding is done with analog circuitry.

95.   What are the advantages of speed control using thyristor?

Advantages :1. Fast Switching Characterstics than Mosfet, BJT, IGBT 2. Low cost 3. Higher

Accuracy.

96.   Why Human body feel Electric shock? and in an Electric train during running , We did not feel any Shock ? why?

Unfortunately our body is a pretty good conductor of electricity, The golden rule is Current takes the lowest resistant path if you have insulation to our feet as the circuit is not complete (wearing rubber footwear which doing some repairs is advisable as our footwear is a high resistance path not much current flows through our body).The electric train is well insulated from its electrical system.

97.   what is the principle of motor?

Whenever a current carrying conductor is placed in an magnetic field it produce turning or twisting movement is called as torque.

98.   Why, when birds sit on transmission lines or current wires doesn't get shock?

Its true that if birds touch the single one line (phase or neutral)they don't get electrical shock...if birds touch 2 lines than the circuit is closed and they get electrical shock.. so if a human touch single one line(phase) then he doesn't get shock if he is in the air (not touching – standing on the ground if he is standing on the ground then touching the line (phase) he will get a shock because the ground on what we standing is like line (ground bed – like neutral)? and in the most of electric lines the neutral is grounded..so that means that human who touch the line closes the circuit between phase and neutral.

99.   what is meant by armature reaction?

The effect of armature flu to main flux is called armature reaction. The armature flux may support main flux or opposes main flux.

100.   what happen if we give 220 volts dc supply to the bulb or tube light?

Bulbs for AC are designed to operate such that it offers high impedance to AC supply.

Normally they have low resistance. When DC supply is applied, due to l w resistance, the current through lamp would be so high that it may damage the bulb element.

101.   Which motor has high Starting Torque and Staring current DC motor, Induction motor Synchronous motor?

DC Series motor has high starting torque. we can not start the Induction motor and Synchronous motors on load, but can not start the DC series motor without load.

102.   what is ACSR cable and where we use it?

ACSR means Aluminium conductor steel reinforced, this conductor is used in transmission & distribution.

103.   What is vaccum currcuit breaker. define with cause and where be use it Device?

A breaker is normally used to break a ciruit. while breaking the circuit, the contact terminals will be separated. At the time of seperation an air gap is formed in between the terminals. Due to existing current flow the air in the gap is ionised and results in the arc. various mediums are used to quench this arc in respective CB's. but in VCB the medium is vaccum gas. since the air in the CB is having vaccum pressure the arc formation is interrupted. VCB's can be used upto kv.

104.   What will happen when power factor is leading in distribution of power? If their is high power factor, i.e if the power factor is close to one:

1.   losses in form of heat will be reduced,

2.   cable becomes less bulky and easy to carry, and very cheap to afford, &

3.   it also reduces over heating of transformers.

105.   whats the one main difference between UPS & inverter ? And electrical engineering & electronics engineering ?

Uninterrupt power supply is mainly use for short time . means according to ups VA it gives backup. ups is also two types : on line and offline . online ups having high volt and amp for long time backup with with high dc voltage. but ups start with 2v dc with 7 amp. but inverter is start with 2v,24,dc to 36v dc and 20amp to 80amp battery with long time backup.

106.   Explain The Flow Of A Typical Instruction Word.?
The flow of a typical Instruction word is as follows:
•   The content of the program counter of 2 byte is transferred to the address register known as MAR (memory address register). This occurs at the starting of a fetch cycle.
•   The contents are transferred via the address bus.
•   Once this is done the timing and control section of the processor reads the contents of the referenced memory address location.
•   After this the data is sent to the memory data register with the help of the data bus.
•   Now the data is placed in the instruction register which will eventually decode and execute it.

107.   Advantages of vvvf drives over non vvvf drives for EOT cranes?
•   Smooth Start And Stop.
•   No Jerking Of Load.
•   Exact Positioning
•   Better Protection For Motor.
•   High/Low Speed Selection.
•   Reliability Of Break Shoe.
•   Programmable Break Control.
•   Easy Circuitry

108.   What is the significance of vector grouping in Power Transformers?

Every power transformer has a vector group listed by its manufacturer. Fundamentally it te s you the information about how the windings are connected (delta or wyes) and the phace difference between the current and voltage. EG. DYN means Delta primary, Wye Secondry and the current is at o clock reffered to the voltage.

109.   Which type of A.C motor is used in the fan (ceiling fan, exhaust fan, padestal fan, b

29

acket fan etc) which are find in the houses ?

Its Single Phase induction motor which mostly squirrel cage type and are capacitor start capacitor run.

110.   Give two basic speed control scheme of DC shunt motor?

By using flux control method: in this method a rheostat is connected across the field winding to control the field current.so by changing the current the flux produced by the field winding can be changed, and since speed is inversely proportional to flux speed can be controlled .armature control method:in this method a rheostat is connected across armature winding by varying the resistance the value of resistive drop(IaRa)can be varied,and since speed is directly proportional to Eb-IaRa the speed can be controlled.
Whenever a current carrying conductor is placed in an magnetic field it produce turning or twisting movement is called as torque.

111.   what is meant by armature reaction?

The effect of armature flu to main flux is called armature reaction. The armature flux may support main flux or opposes main flux.

112.   Give two basic speed control scheme of DC shunt motor?

By using flux control method:in this method a rheostat is connected across the field winding to control the field current.so by changing the current the flux produced by the field winding can be changed, and since speed is inversely proportional to flux speed can be controlled .armature control method:in this method a rheostat is connected across armature wdg. by varying the resistance the value of resistive drop(IaRa)can be varied,and since speed is directly proportional to Eb-IaRa the speed can be controlled.

113.   what is the difference between synchronous generator & asynchronous generator?

In simple, synchronous generator supply's both active and reactive power but asynchronous generator(induction generator) supply's only active power and observe reactive power for magnetizing. This type of generators are used in windmills.

114. What is the Polarization index value ? (pi value)and simple definition of polarization index ?

Its ratio between insulation resistance(IR)i.e meggar value for 0min to insulation resistance for min. It ranges from 5-7 for new motors & normally for motor to be in good condition it should be Greater than .5 .

115. Why syn. generators are used for the production of electricity?

synchronous machines have capability to work on different power factor(or say different imaginary power varying the field emf. Hence syn. Generators are used for the production of electricity.

116. What is the difference between synchronous generator & asynchronous generator?

In simple, synchronous generator supply's both active and reactive power but asynchronous generator(induction generator) supply's only active power and observe reactive power for magnetizing. This type of generators are used in windmills.

117. 1 ton is equal to how many watts?

1 ton = 12000 BTU/hr and to convert BTU/hr to horsepower, 12,000
* 0.000929 = 4.715 hp therefore 1 ton = 4.715*.746 = .5 KW.

118. why syn. generators are used for the production of electricity?

synchronous machines have capability to work on different power facto (or say different imaginary power varying the field emf. Hence syn. Generators are used for the production of electricity.

119. Enlist types of dc generator?

D.C.Generators are classified into two types:

1)separatly exicted d.c.generator 2)self exicted d.c.generator,

which is further classified into;1)series 2)shunt and compound(which is further classified into cumulative and differential).

120.   What is Automatic Voltage regulator(AVR)?

AVR is an abbreviation for Automatic Voltage Regulator. It is important part in Synchronous Generators, it controls the output voltage of the generator by controlling its excitation current. Thus it can control the output Reactive Power of the Generator.

121.   What is an exciter and how does it work?

There are two types of exciters, static exciter and rotory exciter. purpose of excitor is to supply the excitation dc voltage to the fixed poles of generator.Rotory excitor is an additional small generator mounted on the shaft of main generator. if it is dc generator, it will supply dc to the rotory poles through slip ring and brushes(conventional alternator). if it is an ac excitor, out put of ac excitor is rectified by rotating diodes and supply dc to main fixed poles.ac excitor is the ac generator whose field winding are stationary and armature rotates. initial voltage is built up by residual magnetism.It gives the starting torque to the generator.

122.   Difference between a four point starter and three point starter?

The shunt connection in four point stater is provided separately form the line where as in three point stater it is connected with line which is the drawback in three point stater

123.   Why use the VCB at High Transmission System ? Why can't use ACB?

Actually the thing is vacuum has high arc queching property compare to air because in VCB ,the die electric strengths equal to 8 times of air . That y always vaccum used as inHT breaker and air used as in LT .

124.   What is the difference between surge arrestor and lightning arrestor?

LA is installed outside and the effect of lightning is grounded, where as surge arrestor installed inside panels comprising of resistors which consumes the energy and nullify the effect of surge.

125. What happens if i connect a capacitor to a generator load?

Connecting a capacitor across a generator always improves power factor, but it will help depends up on the engine capacity of the alternator, other wise the alternator will be over loaded due to the extra watts consumed due to the improvement on pf. Secondly, don't connect a capacitor across an alternator while it is picking up or without any other load.

126. Explain Briefly What Happens When The Intr Signal Goes High In The 8085?
The INTR is a maskable interrupt for the 8085. It has the lowest priority and is also non vectored. When this INTR signal goes into the high state the following things occur / take place:
• For every instruction that is executed the 8085 checks the status of this interrupt./
• Till an instruction is completed the signal of INTR will remain high. Once an instruction is completed the processor sends an acknowledgement signal INTA.
• As soon as the INTA signal goes low a new opcode is placed on the data bus for transfer.
• Once the new instruction is received the processor saves the address of new instruction into the STACK and an interrupt service subroutine begins.

127. Explain the working principal of the circuit breaker?

Circuit Breaker is one which makes or breaks the circuit. It has two contacts namely fixed contact & moving contact. under normal condition the moving contact World comes in contact with fixed contact there by forming the closed contact for the flow of current. During abnormal & faulty conditions(when current excee s the rated value) an arc is produced between the fixed & moving contacts & thereby it forms the open circuit Arc is extinguished by the Arc Quenching media like air, oil, vaccum etc.

128. How many types of colling system it transformers?
1. ONAN (oil natural,air natural)

2. ONAF (oil natural,air forced)

3. OFAF (oil forced,air forced)

4. ODWF (oil direct,water forced)

5. OFAN (oil forced,air forced)

129. Explain All The Addressing Modes Of The 8085 With The Help Of Examples.?

The various types of addressing modes of the 8085 are as follows:

•   Direct addressing: The instructions in itself contain the opearand. For ex. STA5513H or in/out instructions such as IN PORT C.

•   Register addressing: The general purpose registers contain the operands. For ex. MOV A, B;

•   Register indirect addressing: This involves the use of register pairs instead of a single register. For ex MOV A, M; ADD M.

•   Immediate addressing: The example are MVI A, 07; or ADI 0F etc.

•   Implicit addressing: this form of addressing contains no operands. For ex. RAR, CMA etc.

130. what is stepper motor. what is its uses?

Stepper motor is the electrical machine which act upon input pulse applied to it. it is one type of synchronous motor JNTU which runs in steps in either direction instead of running in complete cycle. so, in automation parts it is used.

131. Tell me in detail about c.t. and p.t. ?

The term Ct. means current transformer, and the term P.T means potential transformer.In circuit where measurements of high voltage and high current is involved they are used there.Particularly when a measuring device like voltmeter or ammeter is not able to measure such high value of quantity because of large value of torque due to such high value it can damage the measuring device.so, CT and PT are introduced in the circuits. They work on the same principle of transformer, which is based on linkage of electromagneticflux produced by primary with secondary.They work on the ratio to they are designed.E.g if CTis of ratio 50005A and it has to measure secondary current of 8000A.then ANS=8000*55000=8Aand this result will be given to ammeter .and after measuring 8A we can calculate the primary current. Same is the operation of PT but measuring voltage.

132. There are a Transformer and an induction machine. Those two have the same supply. For which device the load current will be maximum? And why?

The motor has max load current compare to that of transformer because the motor consumes real power.. and the transformer is only producing the working flux and its not consuming.. hence the load current in the transformer is because of core loss so it is minimum.

133. what is power factor? whether it should be high or low? why?

Power factor should be high in order to get smooth operation of the system. Low power factor means losses will be more. it is the ratio of true power to apparent power. it has to be ideally 1. if it is too low then cable over heating & equipment overloading will occur. if it is greater than 1 then load will act as capacitor and starts feeding the source and will cause tripping.(if pf is poor ex: 0.17 to meet actual power load has to draw more current(V constant),result in more losses if pf is good ex: 0.95 to meet actual power load has to draw less current(V constant),result in less losses).

134. What is the difference between Isolator and Circuit Breaker?

Isolator is a off load device which is used for isolating the down stream circuits from up stream circuits for the reason of any maintenance on downstream circuits. it is manually operated and oes not contain any solenoid unlike circuit breaker. it should not be operated while it is having oad. first the oad on it must be made zero and then it can safely operated. its specification only rated current is given.But circuit breaker is onload automatic device used for breaking the circuit in case of abnormal con itions ike short circuit,
overload etc., it is having three specification 1 is rated current and 2 is sho t ci cuit b eaking capacity and 3 is instantaneous tripping current.

135. what is boucholz relay and the significance of it in to the transformer ?

Boucholz relay is a device which is used for the protection of transformer from its internal faults, it is a gas based relay. whenever any internal fault occurs in a transformer, the boucholz relay at once gives a horn for some time, if the transformer is isolated from the circuit then it stop its sound itself other wise it trips the circuit by its own tripping mechanism.

136.   Name 5 Different Addressing Modes in microprocessor?

Immediate, Direct, Register, Register indirect, Implied addressing modes.

137.   What is frantic effect?

Output voltage is greater than the input voltage receiving end voltage is greater than the sending end voltage.

138.   Mention The Different Types Of Data Transfers Possible In The 8085.?
The various types of data transfer operations possible are:
*   Data transfer is possible between two registers.
*   It is also possible between a memory location and a register.
*   Also it can occur between an input/output device and an accumulator.
*   In reality data is never transferred it can only be copied from one location to another.

139.   Why we do 2 types of earthing on transformer (ie:)body earthing & neutral earthing ,

The two types of earthing are Familiar as Equipment earthing and system earthing.
In Equipment earthing: body (non conducting part)of the equipment shouldd be earthed to safegaurd the human beings.
In system Earthing : In this neutral of the supply source (Transformer or Generator) should be grounded. With this, in case of unbalanced loading neutral will not be shifted.so that unbalanced voltages will not arise. We can protect the equipment also.
With size of the equipment(transformer or alternator)and selection of relying system earthing will be further classified into directly earthed, Impedance earthing, resistive (NGRs) earthing.

140.   What is the difference between MCB & MCCB, Where it can be used?

MCB is miniature circuit breaker which is thermal operated and use for short circuit protection in small current rating circuit. MCCB moulded case circuit breaker and is thermal operated for over load current and magnetic operation for instant trip in short circuit condition.under voltage and under frequency may be inbuilt. Normally it is used where normal current is more than 100.

141.   Where should the lighting arrestor be placed in distribution lines?

Near distribution transformers and out going feeders of 11kv and incoming feeder of 33kv and near power transformers in sub-stations.

142.   Define IDMT relay?

It is an inverse definite minimum time relay.In IDMT relay its operating is inversely proportional and also a characteristic of minimum time after which this relay operates.It is inverse in the sense ,the tripping time will decrease as the magnitude of fault current increase.

143.   What are the transformer losses?

Transformer losses have two sources-copper loss and magnetic loss. Copper losses are caused by the resistance of the wire (I2R). Magnetic losses are caused by e y currents and hysteresis in the core. Copper loss is a constant after the coil has been wound and therefore a measurable loss. Hysteresis loss is constant for a particular voltage and current. Eddy-current loss, however, is different for each frequency passed through the transformer.

144.   What is the count of hvdc transmission lines in India?

At present there are three hvdc transmission lines in india 1)chandrapur to padghe(mumbai)–(100 MW at ±00 kV DC) 2)rehand to delhi (100 MW at ±00 kV DC) 3)talchal to kolar (200 MW)

145.   What is meant by regenerative braking?

When the supply is cut off for a running motor, it still continue running due to inertia. In order to stop it quickly we place a load(resitor) across the armature winding and the motor should have maintained continuous field supply. so that back e.m.f voltage is made to apply across the resistor and due to load the motor stops quickly.This type of breaking is called as "Regenerative Breaking".

146.   Why is the starting current high in a DC motor?

In DC motors, Voltage equation is V=Eb-IaRa (V = Terminal voltage,Eb = Back emf in Motor,Ia = Armature current,Ra = Aramture resistance).At starting, Eb is zero. Therefore, V=IaRa, Ia = V/Ra ,where   Ra is very less like 0.01ohm.i.e, Ia will become enormously increased.

147.   What are the advantages of star-delta starter with induction motor?

(1). the main advantage of using the star delta starter is reduction of current during the starting of the motor.Starting current is reduced to 3-4 times Of current of Direct online starting.(2). Hence the starting current is reduced , the voltage drops during the starting of motor in systems are reduced.

148. Why Delta Star Transformers are used for Lighting Loads?

For lighting loads, neutral conductor is must and hence the secondary must be star winding. and this lighting load is always unbalanced in all three phases. To minimize the current unbalance in the primary we use delta winding in the primary. So delta / star transformer is used for lighting loads.

149. Why in a three pin plug the earth pin is thicker and longer than the other pins?

It depends upon R=rho l/a where area(a) is inversely proportional to resistance (R), so if (a) increases, R decreases & if R is less the leakage current will take low resistance path so the earth pin should be thicker. It is longer because the First to make the connection and Last to disconnect should be earth Pin. This assures Safety for the person who uses the electrical instrument.

150. Why series motor cannot be started on no-load?

Series motor cannot be started without load because of high starting torque. Series motors are used in Trains, Crane etc.

151. Why ELCB can't work if N input of ELCB do not connect to ground?

ELCB is used to detect earth leakage fault. Once the phase and neutral are connected in an ELCB, the current will flow through phase and that much current will have to return neutral so resultant current is zero. Once there is a ground fault in the load side, current from phase will directly pass through earth and it will not return through neutral through ELCB. That means once side current is going and not returning.

Because of this difference in current ELCB will trip and it will safe guard the other circuits from faulty loads. If the neutral is not grounded, fault current will definitely high and that full fault current will come back through ELCB, and there will be no difference in current.

152. How electrical power is generated by an A.C Generator?

For the generation of elect power we need a prime mover which supplies mechanical power input to the alternator, can be steam turbines,or hydro turbines .When poles of the motor moves under the armature conductors which are placed on the stator ,field flux cut the armature conductor ,therefore voltage is generated and is of sinusoidal in nature...due to polarity change of r t r p les(i,e) N-S-N-S.

153. Why an ac solenoid valve attract the plunger even though we interchanges the terminal? Will the poles changes?

Yes because the poles changes for every half-cycle of ac voltage so the polarity f AC voltage is continuously changing for every half cycle. so, interchanging of terminals in ac system es n t sh w any difference. That's why the ac solenoid attract the plunger even though it's terminals are interchanged.

154. What is derating?, why it is necessary, it is same for all means for drives, motors, and cables.

The current currying of cables will change depending upon the site temperature (location of site), type of run (it will run through duct, trench, buried etc.), number of tray, depth of trench, distance between cables.

Considering this condition actual current currying capacity of cable reduce than current currying capacity (which given to cable Catalogue) this is called derating.

155. Why temperature rise is conducted in bus bars and isolators?

Bus bars and isolators are rated for continuous power flow, that means they carry heavy currents which rises their temperature. so it is necessary to test this devices for temperature rise.

156. When voltage increases then current also increases then what is the need of over voltage relay and over current relay? Can we measure over voltage and over current by measuring current only?

We can't sense the over voltage by just measuring the current only because the current increases not only for over voltages but also for under voltage(As most of the loads are non-linear in nature).So, the over voltage protection & over current protection are completely different. Over voltage relay meant for sensing over voltages & protect the system from insulation break down and firing. Over current relay meant for sensing any internal short circuit, over load condition ,earth fault thereby reducing the system failure & risk of fire.So, for   a better protection of the system. It should have both over voltage & over current relay.

157. If one lamp connects between two phases it will glow or not?

If the voltage between the two phase is equal to the lamp voltage then the lamp will glow. When the voltage difference is big it will damage the lamp and when the difference is smaller the lamp will glow depending on the type of lamp.

158.   How do you select a cable size (Cu & Al) for a particular load?

At first calculate the electrical current of the load, after that derate the electrical current considering derating factor(depending on site condition and laying of cable) after choose the cable size from cable catalog considering derating electrical current.After that measure the length of cable required from supply point of load to load poin. Calculate the voltage drop which will max 3% (resistance and reactance of cable found from cable catalog of selecting cable) if voltage drop>3% then choose next higher size of cable.

159. What are HRC fuses and where it is used?

HRC stand for "high rupturing capacity" fuse and it is used in distribution system for electrical transformers.

160. Which power plant has high load factor?

All base load power plants have a high load factor. If we use high efficiency power plants to supply the base load,we can reduce the cost of generation. Hydel power plants have a higher efficiency than thermal & nuclear power plants.

161. Mention the methods for starting an induction motor?

The different methods of starting an induction motor
• Direct online starter
• Star delta starter
• Auto transformer starter Resistance starter
• Series reactor starter

162. What is the difference between earth resistance and earth electrode resistance?

Only one of the terminals is evident in the earth resistance. In order to find the second terminal we should recourse to its definition: Earth Resistance is the resistance existing between the electrically accessible part of a buried electrode and another point of the earth, which is far away.
The resistance of the electrode has the following components:
(A)   the resistance of the metal and that of the connection to it.
(B)   the contact resistance of the surrounding earth to the electrode.

163. What is use of lockout relay in ht voltage?

A lock-out relay is generally placed in line before or after the e-stop switch so the power can be shut off at one central location. this relay is powered by the same electrical source as the control power and is operated by a key lock switch. the relay itself may have up to 24 contact points within the unit itself. This allows the control power for multiple machines to be locked out by the turn of a single key switch.

164. What is the power factor of an alternator at no load?

At no load Synchronous Impedance of the alternator is responsible for creating angle difference. So it should be zero lagging like inductor.

165. How to determine capacitor tolerance codes?

In electronic circuits, the capacitor tolerance can be determined by a code that appears on the casing. The code is a letter that often follows a three-digit number (such as 130Z).The first two are the 1st and 2nd significant digits and the third is a multiplier code. Most of the time the last digit tells you how many zeros to write after the first two digits and these are read as Pico-Farads.

166. Why most of analog o/p devices having o/p range 4 to 20 mA and not 0 to 20 mA?

4-20 mA is a standard range used to indicate measured values for any process. The reason that 4ma is chosen instead of 0 mA is for fail safe operation .For example- a pressure instrument gives output 4mA to indicate 0 psi, up to 20 mA to indicate 100 psi, or full scale. Due to any problem in instrument (i.e) broken wire, its output reduces to 0 mA. So if range is 0-20 mA then we can differentiate whether it is due to broken wire or due to 0 psi.

167. Briefly Explain The Steps Involved In A Fetch Cycle.?
Fetch cycle is the time required to fetch an opcode from a particular location in memory.
• General Fetch Cycles consist of 3T states.
• The first T state involves the sending of the memory address stored in the Program

Counter to the memory.

•   During the second T state the contents of the addressed memory is read (this generally is the opcode at the specified location)

•   In the third T state the opcode is sent to the Instruction register through the data bus for execution.

•   For slower memories the processors has the provision to get in to the WAIT cycles as well.

168.   What is meant by knee point voltage?

Knee point voltage is calculated for electrical Current transformers and is very important factor to choose a CT. It is the voltage at which a CT gets saturated.(CT-current transforme).

169.   What is reverse power relay?

Reverse Power flow relay are used in generating stations's protection. A generating stations is supposed to fed power to the grid and in case generating units are off, there is no generation in the plant then plant may take power from grid. To stop the flow of power from grid to generator. we use reverse power relay.

170.   What is the difference between isolators and –>electrical circuit breakers? What is bus-bar?

Isolators are mainly for switching purpose under normal conditions but they cannot operate in fault conditions
.Actually they used for isolating the CBs for maintenance. Whereas CB gets activated under fault conditions according to the fault detected. Bus bar is nothing but a junction where the power is getting distributed for independent loads.

171.   What are the advantage of free wheeling diode in a Full Wave rectifier?

Free wheeling diode improve the power factor of the system and also increases the system efficiency.

172.   What is the function of interposing current transformer?

The main function of an interposing current transformer is to balance the currents supplied to the relay where there would otherwise be an imbalance due to the ratios of the main current transformers. Interposing current transformer are equipped with a wide range of taps that can be selected by the user to achieve the balance required.

173.   What are Motor Generator Sets? Explain the different ways the motor generator set can be used.

Motor Generator Sets are a combination of an electrical generator and an engine mounted together to form a single piece of equipment. Motor generator set is also referred to as a genset, or more commonly, a generator. The motor generator set can used in the following different ways:
1.Alternating current (AC) to direct current (DC)
2.DC to AC
3.DC at one voltage to DC at another voltage
4.AC at one frequency to AC at another harmonically-related frequency

174. What is power quality meter ?

Power Quality meters are common in many industrial environments. Small units are now available for home use as well. They give operators the ability to monitor the both perturbations on the power supply, as well as power used within a building, or by a single machine or appliance. In some situations, equipment function and   operation is monitored and controlled from a remote location where communication is via modem, or high- speed communication lines. So we can understand the importance of power measurement through power quality meters.

175. What is the different between digital phase converter and ordinary phase converter?

Digital phase converter are a recent development in phase converter technology that utilizes proprietary   software in a powerful microprocessor to control solid state power switching components. This microprocessor, called a digital signal processor (DSP), monitors the phase conversion process, continually adjusting the input and output modules of the converter to maintain perfectly balanced three-phase power under all load conditions.

176. Explain the operation of variable frequency transformer?

A variable frequency transformer is used to transmit electricity between two asynchronous a treating current domains. A variable frequency transformer is a doubly-fed electric machine esemb ing a vertical shaft hydroelectric generator with a three-phase wound rotor, connected by sliprings to one external ac power circuit. A direct-current torque motor is mounted on the same shaft. Changing the direction of torque applied to the shaft changes the direction of power flow; with no applied torque, the shaft rotates due to the difference in frequency between the networks connected to the rotor and stat .The variable frequency transformer behaves as a continuously adjustable phase-shifting transformer. It allows control of the power flow between two networks

177. What is the main use of rotary phase converter ?

Rotary phase converter will be converting single phase power into true balanced 3 phase power, so it is often called as single phase to three phase converter . Often the advantages of 3 phase motors, and other 3 phase equipment, make it worthwhile to convert single phase to 3 phase so that small and large consumers need not want to pay for the extra cost of a 3 phase service but may still wish to use 3 phase equipment.

178. Use of switch mode power converter in real-time basis?

Switch mode power converter can be used in the following 5 different ways
1)   step down an unregulated dc input voltage to produce a regulated dc output voltage using a circuit known as Buck Converter or Step-Down SMPS,
2)   step up an unregulated dc input voltage to produce a regulated dc output voltage using a circuit known as Boost Converter or Step-Up SMPS,
3)   step up or step down an unregulated dc input voltage to produce a regulated dc output voltage, 4)invert the input dc voltage using usually a circuit such as the Cuk converter, and
5) produce multiple dc outputs using a circuit such as the fly-back converter.

179. Which type of oil is used as a transformer oil?

Transformer oil, or insulating oil, is usually a highly-refined mineral oil that is stable at high temperatures and has excellent electrical insulating properties. It is used in oil filled transformers, some types of high voltage capacitors, fluorescent lamp ballasts, and some types of high voltage switches and circuit breakers. Its functions are to insulate, suppress corona and arcing, and to serve as a coolant.

Well into the 170s, polychlorinated biphenyls (PCB)s were often used as a dielectric fluid since they are not flammable. They are toxic, and under incomplete combustion, can form highly toxic products such as furan. Starting in the early 170s, concerns about the toxicity of PCBs have led to their banning in many countries.

Today, non-toxic, stable silicon-based or fluoridated hydrocarbons are used, where the added expense of a fire- resistant liquid offsets additional building cost for a transformer vault. Combustion-resistant vegetable oil-based dielectric coolants and synthetic pentaerythritol tetra fatty acid (C7, C8) esters are also becoming increasingly common as alternatives to naphthenic mineral oil. Esters are non-toxic to aquatic life, readily biodegradable,   and have a lower volatility and higher flash points than mineral oil.

180.   If we give 2334 A, 540V on Primary side of 1.125 MVA step up transformer, then what will be the Secondary Current, If Secondary Voltage=11 KV?

As we know the Voltage & current relation for transformer-$V1/V2 = I2/I1$
We Know, $V1= 540$ V; $V2=11KV$ or 11000 V; $I1= 2334$ Amps.
By putting these value   on Relation - $540/11000= I2/2334$ So,$I2 = 114.5$ Amps

181.   what are the points to be consider for MCB(miniature circuit breaker selection?

$I(L)*1.25=I(MAX)$ maximum current. Mcb specification are done on maximum current flow in circuit.

182.   what is the full form of KVAR?

We know there are three types of power in Electrical as Active, apparent & reactive. So

KVAR is stand for "Kilo Volt Amps with Reactive component.

183.   What is excitation?

Excitation is applying an external voltage to DC shunt coil in DC motors.

184.   In three pin plug 6 Amp. 220v AC rating. why earth pin diameter is higher than other two   pin? what its purpose ?

Because Current flow in the conductor is inversely proportional to the conductor diameter. So if any short circuits occur in the system first high currents bypassed in the Earthling terminal.(R=Pl/a a ea of the conductor increases resistance value decreases)

185.   Difference between megger test equipment and contact resistance meter test instruments?

Megger test equipment used to measure cable electric resistance, conductor continuity, phase identification where as contact resistance meter test instruments used to measure low resistance like relays , contactors.

186.   When we connect the large capacitor bank in series?

we connect large capacitor bank in series to improve the voltage power supply at the load end in balanced transmission line when there is considerable voltage drop along the balanced transmission line due to high impedance of the line. So in order to bring the voltage at the load terminals within its limits (i.e (+ or – %6)of the rated high terminal voltage)the large capacitor bank is used in series.

187.   What is electrical diversity factor in electrical installations?

Electrical diversity factor is the ratio of the sum of the individual maximum demands of the various subdivisions of a system, or part of a system, to the maximum demand of the whole system, or part of the system, under consideration. Electrical diversity factor is usually more than one.

188.   Why field rheostat is kept in minimum position while armature rheostat at maximum position?

In motors at the time of starting the armature resistance is introduced to reduce the high starting current and the field resistance is kept minimum to have high starting torque.

189.   Why computer humming sound occurred in HT transmission line?

This computer humming sound is coming due to ionization (breakdown of air into charged particles) of air around transmission conductor. This effect is called as Corona effect, and it is considered as power loss.

190.   What Are Input & Output Devices?

Keyboards, Floppy disk are the examples of input devices. Printer, LED / LCD display, CRT Monitor are the examples of output devices.

191.   What is different between resistance grounding system and resistance earthing system?

Resistance grounding system means connecting the neutral point of the load to the ground to carry the residual current in case of unbalanced conditions through the neutral to the ground whereas resistance earthing system is done in an electric equipment in order to protect he equipment in occurrence of fault in the system.

192.   Why should be the frequency 50 Hz 60Hz only why not others like 45, 95 56 or anything , why should we maintain the frequency constant if so why it is only 50 Hz 60Hz?

We can have the frequency at any frequency you like, but than you must also make your own motors,high voltage transformers or any other equipment you want to use.We maintain the frequency at 50hz or 60hz because the world maintains a standard at 50 /60hz and the equipments are are made to operate at these frequency.

193.   How to determine alternating current frequency?

Zero crossings of the sine wave to trigger a monostable (pulse generator) is a way to determine alternating current frequency. A fixed width pulse is generated for each cycle. Thus there are "n" pulses per second, each with with a constant energy. The more pulses there are per second, them or the energy. The pulses are integrated (filtered or averaged) to get a steady DC voltage which is proportional to frequency. This voltage can then be displayed on an analogue or digital voltmeter, indicating frequency. This method is more suitable than a direct counter, as it can get good accuracy in a second so.

194.   Why electricity in India is in the multiples of 11 like 11kv, 22kv, 33kv ?

Transformer Induced voltage equation contains 4.44 factor. $E=4.44*f*T*phi$
E -Induced emf per phase T
-number of turns f -frequency
phi -maximum flux per pole
From the equation we see that E is proportional to 4.4 and it is in turn multiple f 11. So always transmission voltage is multiple of 11

195.   Why we use ac system in India why not dc ?

Firstly, the output of power stations comes from a rotary turbine, which by it's nature is AC and therefore requires no power electronics to convert to DC. Secondly it is much easier to change the voltage of AC electricity for transmission and distribution. Thirdly the cost of plant associated with AC transmission (circuit breakers, transformers etc) is much lower than the equivalent of DC transmission AC transmission provides a number of technical advantages. When a fault on the network occurs, a large fault current occurs. In an AC system this becomes much easier to interrupt, as the sine wave current will naturally tend to zero at some point making the current easier to interrupt.

196.   Which type of motor is used in trains, what is the rating of supply used explain Working principal?

Dc series is in the trains to get high starting torque while starting of the trains and operating voltage is 1500v dc.

197. Battery banks are in connected in series or parallel and why?

Battery banks are always connected in series in order to get a multiplied voltage where the AH or current capacity remaining same. Ex : 24 nos. 2V,200Ah batteries connected in series will give 48V,200Ah output (AH= Ampere hours)

198. What is inrush current?

Inrush current is the current drawn by a piece of electrically operated equipment when power is first applied. It can occur with AC or DC powered equipment, and can happen even with low supply voltages.

199. In a Tap changing transformer where is the tap connected, is it connected in the primary side or secondary side?

Tapings are connected to high voltage winding side, because of low current. If we connect tapings to low voltage side, sparks will produce while tap changing operation due to high current

200. Why transformer ratings are in kva?

Since the power factor of transformer is dependent on load we only define VA rating and does not include power factor .In case of motors, power factor depend on construction and hence rating of motors is in KWatts and include power factor.

201. What is difference between fuse and breaker?

Fuses are burned at the time of over current flows in the circuit but breakers are just open(not burn) at the time of over current flow. Fuses are used in only one time but breakers are used by multiple number of times.

202. What is the difference between delta-delta, delta-star transformer?

As we know that Electrical is having two type of load, Active and Reactive .Capacitor is reeactive load which is Delta-delta transformer is used at generating station or a receiving station for Change of Voltage (i,e) generally it is used where the Voltage is high & Current is low. Delta-star is a distribution kind of transformer where from secondary star neutral is taken as a return path and this configuration is used for Step own voltage phenomena.

203. What's electric traction?

Traction implies with the electric power for traction system i. e. f railways, trams, tr lleys etc. electric traction implies use of the electricity for all these. Now a day, magnetic traction is also utilised for bullet trains.Essentially dc motors are utilized for electric traction systems.

204. Can An Rc Circuit Be Used As Clock Source For 8085?

Yes, it can be used, if an accurate clock frequency is not required. Also, the component cost is low compared to LC or Crystal.

205. Define stepper motor. What is the use of stepper motor?

The motor which work or act on the applied input pulse in it, is called as stepper motor.This stepper motor is under the category of synchronous motor, which often does not fully depend of complete cycle. It likes to works in either direction related to steps. for this purpose it mainly used in automation parts.

206. What is a differential amplifier? Also, explain CMRR.

Differential Amplifier: he amplifier, which is used to amplify the voltage difference between two input-lines neither of which is grounded, is called differential amplifier. This reduces the amount of noise which is injected into the amplifier, because any noise appearing simultaneously on both the input-terminals as the amplifying circuitry rejects it being a common mode signal.

CMRR: It can be defined as the ratio of differential voltage-gain to common made voltage gain. If a differential amplifier is perfect, CMRR will be infinite because in that case common mode voltage gain would be zero.

207. What is use of lockout relay in ht voltage?

A lock-out relay is generally placed in line before or after the e-stop switch so the power can be shut off at one central location. This relay is powered by the same electrical source as the control power which is operated by a key lock switch. The relay itself may have up to 24 contact points within the unit itself. This allows the control power for multiple machines to be locked out by the turn of a single key switch.

208. How can you start-up the 40w tube light with 230v AC/DC without using any choke/Coil?

It's possible with Electronic choke. Otherwise it's not possible to ionize the particles in tube light, with normal voltage.

209. What types domain of Laplace transforms? What behavior can Laplace transform predict how the system work?

Types domain of Laplace transforms is s-domain, Laplace transforms provide a method to find position, acceleration or voltage the system will have.

210. In the magnetic fluxes, what is the role of armature reaction?

The armature flux has an important role for the running condition. This armature flux can oppose the main flux or it may support the main flux for better running condition. This effect of supporting and opposing of main flux to armature flux is called armature reaction.

211. Explain thin film resistors and wire-wound resistors

Thin film resistors- It is constructed as a thin film of resistive material is deposited on an insulating substrate. Desired results are obtained by either trimming the layer thickness or by cutting helical grooves of suitable pitch along its length. During this process, the value of the resistance is monitored closely and cutting of grooves is stopped as soon as the desired value of resistance is obtained.

Wire wound resistors – length of wire wound around an insulating cylindrical co e a e known as wire wound resistors. These wires are made of materials such as Constantan and Managing because of their high resistivity, and low temperature coefficients. The complete wire wound resistor is coated with an insulating material such as baked enamel

212. whats the one main difference between UPS & inverter ? And elect ical enginee ing & electronics engineering ?

Uninterrupt power supply is mainly use for short time . means according to ups VA it gives backup. ups is also two types : on line and offline .online ups having high volt and amp f l ng time backup with with high dc voltage. but ups start with v dc with 7 amp. but inverter is start with v,24,dc to 36v dc and 0amp to 180amp battery with long time backup.

213. What are the operation carried out in Thermal power station?

The water is obtained in the boiler and the coal is burnt so that steam is obtained this steam is allowed to hit the turbine, the turbine which is coupled with the generator generates the electricity

214. What is the difference between Electronic regulator and ordinary rheostat regulator for

fans?

The difference between the electronic and ordinary regulator is the fact that in electronic reg. power losses tend to be less because as we minimize the speed the electronic reg. give the power necessary for that particular speed but in case of ordinary rheostat type reg. the power wastage is same for every speed and no power is saved. In electronic regulator triac is employed for speed control. by varying the firing angle speed is controlled but in rheostatic control resistance is decreased by steps to achieve speed control.

215. What is 2 phase motor?

A two phase motor is often a motor with the the starting winding and the running winding have a phase split. e. g; ac servo motor. where the auxiliary winding and the control winding have a phase split of 90 degree.

216. What does quality factor depend on resonance?

Quality factor depends on frequency and bandwidth.

217. What are the types of power in electrical power?

There are normally three types of power are counted in electrical power. They are,
• Apparent power
• Active power
• Reactive power

218. What are the advantages of VSCF wind electrical system?

Advantages of VSCF wind electrical system are:
• No complex pitch changing mechanism is needed.
• Aero turbine always keeps going at maximum efficiency point.
• Extra energy in the high wind speed region of the speed – duration curve can be extracted
• Significant reduction in aerodynamic stresses, which are associated with constant –

speed operation.

219. What is slip in an induction motor?

Slip can be defined as the distinction between the flux speed (Ns) and the rotor speed (N). Speed of the rotor of an induction motor is always less than its synchronous speed. It is usually expressed as a percentage of synchronous speed (Ns) and represented by the symbol 'S'.

220. Why link is provided in neutral of an ac circuit and fuse in phase of ac circuit?

Link is provided at a Neutral common point in the circuit from which various connection are taken for the individual control circuit and so it is given in a link form to withstand high Amps. But in the case of Fuse in the Phase of AC circuit it is designed such that the fuse rating is calculated for the particular circuit (i.e load) only. So if any malfunction happen the fuse connected in the particular control circuit a one without off.

221. State the difference between generator and alternator?

Generator and alternator are two devices, which converts mechanical energy into electrical energy. Both have the same principle of electromagnetic induction, the only difference is that their construction. Generator persists stationary magnetic field and rotating conductor which lls n the armature with slip rings and brushes riding against each other, hence it converts the induced emf into dc current f r external load whereas an alternator has a stationary armature and rotating magnetic field for high voltages but for low voltage output rotating armature and stationary magnetic field is used.

222. What is ACSR cable and where we use it?

ACSR means Aluminium conductor steel reinforced, this conductor is used in transmission & distribution.

223. What Does Quality Factor Mean?

The Quality factor is also defined, as Q. So it is a number, which reflects the lossness of a circuit. Higher the Q, the lower are the losses.

224.   Why Crystal Is A Preferred Clock Source?

Because of high stability, large Q (Quality Factor) & the frequency that doesn't drift with aging. Crystal is used as a clock source most of the times.

225.   Why use the VCB at High transmission System ? Why can't use ACB?

Actually the thing is vacuum has high arc queching property compare to air because in VCB , the die electric strengths equal to 8 times of air . That y always vaccum used as in HT breaker and air used as in LT .

226.   What Differences Can You State Between The Hlt And Hold States?
•   The Hold is a hardware input whereas HLT is a software instruction.
•   When the HLT state is executed the processor simply stops and the buses are driven to tri state. No form of acknowledgement signal is given out by the processor.
•   In case of HOLD the processor goes into hold state but the buses are not driven to tri state.
•   When the processor goes into the HOLD state it gives out an HLDA signal. This signal can be made to use by other devices.

227.   Does The 8085 Support Externally Initiated Operations? If Yes How?

Yes the 8085 does support several externally initiated operations. The possible operations and the corresponding pins for them in the 8085 are as follows:
•   It supports resetting (this is possible with the Reset Pin).
•   Various interruptions (these are possible through Trap, RST 7.5, 6.5, 5.5 and the interrupt pins.)
•   The 8085 also supports Readying with the help pf the Ready pin.
•   It also has a HOLD pin which can basically pause the operation till required/ as required.

228.   What is Control System?

In a System the output and inputs are interrelated in such a manner that the output quantity or variable is controlled by input quantity, then such a system is called Control System.
The output quantity is called controlled variable or response and the input quantity is called command signal or excitation.

229.   What are different types of Control Systems?

Two major types of Control Systems are 1) Open loop Control System 2) Closed Loop Control Systems. Open loop Control Systems: The Open loop Control System is one in which the Output Quantity has no effect on the Input Quantity. No feedback is present from the output quantity to the input quantity for correction. Closed Loop Control System: The Closed loop Control System is one in which the feedback is provided from the Output quantity to the input quantity for the correction so as to maintain the desired output of the system.

230.   What is a feedback in Control System?

The Feedback in Control System in one in which the output is sampled and proportional signal is fed back to the input for automatic correction of the error (any change in desired output) for further processing to get back the desired output.

231.   Why Negative Feedback is preffered in the Control System?

The role of Feedback in control system is to take the sampled output back to the input and compare output signal with input signal for error (deviation from the desired result).
Negative Feedback results in the better stability of the system and rejects any disturbance signals and is less sensitive to the parameter variations. Hence in control systems negative feedback is considered.

232.   What is the effect of positive feedback on stability of the system?

Positive feedback is not used generally in the control system because it increases the error signal and drives the system to instability. But positive feedbacks are used in minor loop control systems to amplify certain internal signals and parameters

233.   What is Latching current?

Gate signal is to be applied to the thyristor to trigger the thyristor ON in safe mode. When the thyristor starts conducting the forward current above the minimum value, called Latching current, the gate signal which is applied to trigger the device in no longer require to keep the scr in ON position.

234.   What is Holding current ?

When scr is conducting current in forward conduction state, scr will return to forward blocking state when the anode current or forward current falls below a low level called Holding current
Latching current and Holding current are not same. Latching current is associated with the turn on process of the scr whereas holding current is associated with the turn off process. In general holding current will be slightly lesser than the latching current.

235.   Why thyristor is considered as Charge controlled device?

During the triggering process of the thyristor from forward blocking state to forward conduction state through the gate signal, by applying the gate signal (voltage between gate and cathode) increases the minority carrier density in the p-layer and thereby facilitate the reverse break over of the junction J2 and thyristor starts conducting. Higher the magnitude of the gate current pulse, lesser is the time required to inject the charge and turning on the scr. By controlling the amount of charge we can control the turning on time of the scr.

236.   What are the different losses that occur in thyristor while operating?

Different losses that occur are
a)Forward conduction losses during conduction of the thyristor
b)Loss due to leakage current during forward and reverse blocking.
c)Power loss at gate or Gate triggering loss.
d)Switching losses at turn-on and turn-off.

237.   What is meant by knee point voltage?

Knee point voltage is calculated for electrical Current transformers and is very important factor to choose a CT. It is the voltage at which a CT gets saturated.(CT-current transformer).

238.   What is reverse power relay?

Reverse Power flow relay are used in generating stations's protection. A generating stations is supposed to fed power to the grid and in case generating units are off,there is no generation in the plant then plant may take power from grid. To stop the flow of power from grid to generator we use reverse power relay.

239.   What will happen if DC supply is given on the primary of a transformer?

Mainly transformer has high inductance and low resistance.In case of DC supply there is no inductance ,only resistance will act in the electrical circuit. So high electrical current will flow through primary side of the transformer.So for this reason coil and insulation will burn out.

240.   What is the difference between isolators and electrical circuit breakers? What is bus-bar?

Isolators are mainly for switching purpose under normal conditions but they cannot operate in fault conditions .Actually they used for isolating the CBs for maintenance. Whereas CB gets activated under fault conditions according to the fault detected.Bus bar is nothing but a junction where the power is getting distributed for independent loads.

241.   What are the advantage of free wheeling diode in a Full Wave rectifier?

It reduces the harmonics and it also reduces sparking and arching across the mechanical switch so that it reduces the voltage spike seen in a inductive load.

242.   What Are Wait States In Microprocessors, Explain.?

- The WAIT state plays a significant role in preventing CPU speed incompatibilities.
- Many a times the processor is at a ready state to accept data from a device or location, but there might be no input available. This can lead to wastage of cpu time.
- So in such cases when the cpu is ready for an input but there is no such valid data then the system gets into WAIT state. In this scenario the pin 35 (ready pin)is put into a low state.
- As soon as there is some valid data for the 8085 the system comes off the WAIT state and the low state of the READY pin is withdrawn.

243. What is the power factor of an alternator at no load?

At no load Synchronous Impedance of the alternator is responsible for creating angle difference. So it should be zero lagging like inductor.

244. What is the function of anti-pumping in circuit breaker?

When breaker is close at one time by close push button,the anti pumping contactor prevent re close the breaker by close push button after if it already close.

245. What is stepper motor.what is its uses?

Stepper motor is the electrical machine which act upon input pulse applied to it. it is one type of synchronous motor which runs in steps in either direction instead of running in complete cycle.so, in automation parts it is used.

246. There are a Transformer and an induction machine. Those two have the same supply. For which device the load current will be maximum? And why?

The motor has max load current compare to that of transformer because the motor consumes real power.. and the transformer is only producing the working flux and its not consuming.. hence the load current in the transformer is because of core loss so it is minimum.

247. What Are The Boons And Banes Of Having More General Purpose Registers In A

Microprocessor.?

- If there are more general purpose registers the program writing process is more flexible and convenient.
- The number of bits that would be required to detect the registers would increase with more registers, this results in the lowering of the number of operations.
- When a program would involve CALL subroutines the status of the registers would have to be saved and restored often, this would result in a significant overhead for the processor.
- Higher the number of these registers mores space would be used by them on the chip. This can create problems in adding / implementing other functions on the chip..

248.   What is ferrantic effect?

Output voltage is greater than the input voltage or receiving end voltage is greater than the sending end voltage.

249.   What is meant by insulation voltage in cables? explain it?

It is the property of a cable by virtue of it can withstand the applied voltage without rupturing it is known as insulation level of the cable.

250.   What is the difference between MCB & MCCB, Where it can be used?

MCB is miniature circuit breaker which is thermal operated and use for short circuit protection in small current rating circuit. MCCB moulded case circuit breaker and is thermal operated for over load current and magnetic operation for instant trip in short circuit condition.under voltage and under frequency may be inbuilt. Normally it is used where normal current is more than 100A.

251. Where should the lighting arrestor be placed in distribution lines?

Near distribution transformers and out going feeders of 11kv and incomming feeder of 33kv and near power transformers in sub-stations.

252. Define IDMT relay?

It is an inverse definite minimum time relay.In IDMT relay its operating is inversely proportional and also a characteristic of minimum time after which this relay operates.It is inverse in the sense ,the tripping time will decrease as the magnitude of fault current increase.

253. What are the transformer losses?

Transformer losses have two sources-copper loss and magnetic loss. Copper losses are caused by the resistance of the wire (I2R). Magnetic losses are caused by eddy currents and hysteresis in the core. Copper loss is a constant after the coil has been wound and therefore a measurable loss. Hysteresis loss is constant for a particular voltage and current. Eddy-current loss, however, is different for each frequency passed through the transformer.

254. What Are Level-triggering Interrupt?

RST 6.5 & RST 5.5 are level-triggering interrupts

255. How Can Signals Be Classified For The 8085 Microprocessor?

The signals of the 8085 microprocessor based on their functions can be classified into 7 categories namely:
- Frequency and power signals
- Address and data buses

- The control bus
- Interrupt Signals
- Serial Input / Output signals
- DMA signals
- Reset Signals

256.   Why temperature rise is conducted in bus bars and isolators?

Bus bars and isolators are rated for continuous power flow, that means they carry heavy currents which rises their temperature. so it is necessary to test this devices for temperature rise.

257.   What is the difference between synchronous generator & asynchronous generator?

In simple, synchronous generator supply's both active and reactive power but asynchronous generator(induction generator) supply's only active power and observe reactive power for magnetizing. This type of generators are used in windmills.

258.   What is Automatic Voltage regulator(AVR)?

AVR is an abbreviation for Automatic Voltage Regulator.It is important part in Synchronous Generators, it controls theoutput voltage of the generator by controlling its excitation current. Thus it can control the output Reactive Power of the Generator.

259.   Difference between a four point starter and three point starter?

The shunt connection in four point stater is provided separately form the line where as in three point stater it is connected with line which is the drawback in three point stater

260.   Why the capacitors works on ac only?

Generally capacitor gives infinite resistance to dc components(i.e., block the dc components). it allows the ac components to pass through.

261.   How many types of colling system it transformers?

ONAN (oil natural,air natural)
ONAF (oil natural,air forced)
OFAF (oil forced,air forced)
ODWF (oil direct,water forced)
OFAN (oil forced,air forced)

262.   Operation carried out in Thermal power stations?

The water is obtained in the boiler and the coal is burnt so that steam is obtained this steam is allowed to hit the turbine , the turbine which is coupled with the generator generates the electricity.

263.   Explain In Brief The Control And Timing Circuitry Of The 8085.?

•   The timing and control circuitry section of the 8085 is responsible for the generation of timing and control signals so that instructions can be executed.
•   The types of signals involved are : Clock signals, Control signals, Status signals, DMA signals and also the reset section.
•   It is responsible for the fetching and the decoding of the various operations.
•   This section also aids in the generations of control signals for the executions of instructions and for the sync between external devices.

264.   What is the principle of motor?

Whenever a current carrying conductor is placed in an magnetic field it produce turning or twisting movement is called as torque.

265.   What is meant by armature reaction?

The effect of armature flu to main flux is called armature reaction. The armature flux may support main flux or opposes main flux.

266.   What is the difference between synchronous generator & asynchronous generator?

In simple, synchronous generator supply's both active and reactive power but asynchronous generator(induction generator) supply's only active power and observe reactive power for magnetizing.This type of generators are used in windmills.

267.   Whats is MARX CIRCUIT?

It is used with generators for charging a number of capacitor in parallel and discharging them in series.It is used when voltage required for testing is higher than the available.

268.   What are the advantages of speed control using thyristor?

Advantages :
*   Fast Switching Characterstics than Mosfet, BJT, IGBT
*   Low cost
*   Higher Accurate.

269.   What is ACSR cable and where we use it?

ACSR means Aluminium conductor steel reinforced, this conductor is used in transmission & distribution.

270.   Whats the one main difference between UPS & inverter ? And electrical engineering & electronics engineering ?

Uninterrupt power supply is mainly use for short time . means according to ups VA it gives backup. ups is also two types : on line and offline . online ups having high volt and amp for long time backup with with high dc voltage.but ups start with 12v dc with 7 amp. but inverter is startwith 12v,24,dc to 36v dc and 120amp to 180amp battery with long time backup.

271.   What will happen when power factor is leading in distribution of power?

If their is high power factor, i.e if the power factor is close to one:

a)Losses in form of heat will be reduced,

b)Cable becomes less bulky and easy to carry, and very cheap to afford, &

c)It also reduces over heating of tranformers.

272. What are the advantages of star-delta starter with induction motor?

(1). The main advantage of using the star delta starter is reduction of current during the starting of the motor.Starting current is reduced to 3-4 times Of current of Direct online starting.(2). Hence the starting current is reduced , the voltage drops during the starting of motor in systems are reduced.

273. Why Delta Star Transformers are used for Lighting Loads?

For lighting loads, neutral conductor is must and hence the secondary must be star winding. and this lighting load is always unbalanced in all three phases. To minimize the current unbalance in the primary we use delta winding in the primary. So delta / star transformer is used for lighting loads.

274. Why computer humming sound occurred in HT transmission line?

This computer humming sound is coming due to ionization (breakdown of air into charged particles) of air around transmission conductor. This effect is called as Corona effect, and it is considered as power loss.

275. What is rated speed?

At the time of motor taking normal current (rated current)the speed of the motor is called rated speed. It is a speed at which any system take small current and give maximum efficiency.

276. If one lamp connects between two phases it will glow or not?

If the voltage between the two phase is equal to the lamp voltage then the lamp will glow.

When the voltage difference is big it will damage the lamp and when the difference is smaller the lamp will glow depending on the type of lamp.

277.   What are the different operation regions of the SCR?

SCR or thyristor will have three regions of operations based on the mode in which the device is connected in the circuit.

Reverse blocking region: When the cathode of the thyristor is made positive with respect to the anode and no gate signal is applied. In this region scr exhibits the reverse blocking characteristics similar to diode.

Forward blocking region: In this region the anode of the thyristor is made positive with respect to the cathode and no gate signal is applied to the thyristor. A small leakage current flow in this mode of operation of the thyristor

Forward conduction region: when the forward voltage applied between the anode and cathode increases at particular break over voltage avalanche breakdown takes place and thyristor starts conducting current in forward direction. By this type of triggering the device damages the scr. Hence a gate signal is applied before the forward break over voltage to trigger the scr.

278.   What is Latching current?

Gate signal is to be applied to the thyristor to trigger the thyristor ON in safe mode. When the thyristor starts conducting the forward current above the minimum value, called Latching current, the gate signal which is applied to trigger the device in no longer require to keep the scr in ON position.

279.   What is Holding current ?

When scr is conducting current in forward conduction state, scr will return to forward blocking state when the anode current or forward current falls below a low level called Holding current.Latching current and Holding current are not same. Latching current is associated with the turn on process of the scr whereas holding current is associated with the turn off process. In general holding current will be slightly lesser than the latching current.

280.   Why thyristor is considered as Charge controlled device?

During the triggering process of the thyristor from forward blocking state to forward conduction state through the gate signal, by applying the gate signal (voltage between gate and cathode) increases the minority carrier density in the p-layer and thereby facilitate the reverse break over of the junction J2 and thyristor starts conducting. Higher the magnitude of the gate current pulse, lesser is the time required to inject the charge and turning on the scr. By controlling the amount of charge we can control the turning on time of the scr.

281.   What is the relation between the gate signal and forward break over voltage (VBO)?

Thyristor can be triggered by increasing the forward voltage between anode and cathode, at forward break over voltage thyristor starts conducting. However this process may damage the thyristor, so thyristor is advices to trigger on through the gate pulse. When a gate signal is applied thyristor turns on before reaching the break over voltage. Forward voltage at which the thyristor triggers on depends on the magnitude of the gate current. Higher is the gate current lower is the forward break over voltage

282.   What are the different losses that occur in thyristor while operating?

Different losses that occur are
•   Forward conduction losses during conduction of the thyristor
•   Loss due to leakage current during forward and reverse blocking.
•   Power loss at gate or Gate triggering loss.
•   Switching losses at turn-on and turn-off.

283.   What are the advantages of speed control using thyristor?

Advantages : Fast Switching Characteristics than MOSFET, BJT, IGBT Low cost 3. Higher Accurate.

284.   What happens if i connect a capacitor to a generator load?

Connecting a capacitor across a generator always improves powerfactor, but it will help depends up on the engine capacity of the alternator, other wise the alternator will be over loaded due to the extra watts consumed due to the improvement on pf. Secondly, don't connect a capacitor across an alternator while it is picking up or without any other load.

285.   Mention The Various Functional Blocks Of The 8085 Microprocessor.?

The various functional blocks of the 8085 microprocessor are:
*   Registers
*   Arithmetic logic unit
*   Address buffer
*   Increment / decrement address latch
*   Interrupt control
*   Serial I/O control
*   Timing and control circuitry
*   Instructions decoder and machine cycle encoder.

286.   Explain the working principal of the circuit breaker?

Circuit Breaker is one which makes or breaks the circuit. It has two contacts namely fixed contact & moving contact under normal condition the moving contact comes in contact with fixed contact thereby forming the closed contact for the flow of current. During abnormal & faulty conditions (when current exceeds the rated value) an arc is produced between the fixed & moving contacts & thereby it forms the open circuit Arc is extinguished by the Arc Quenching media like air, oil, vacuum etc.

287.   What is the difference between Isolator and Circuit Breaker?

Isolator is a off load device which is used for isolating the downstream circuits from upstream circuits for the reason of any maintenance on downstream circuits. it is manually operated and does not contain any solenoid unlike circuit breaker. it should not be operated while it is having load. first the load on it must be made zero and then it can safely operated. its specification only rated current is given. But circuit breaker is onload automatic device used for breaking the circuit in case of abnormal conditions like short circuit, overload etc., it is having three specification 1 is rated current and 2 is short circuit breaking capacity and 3 is instantaneous tripping current.

288. What is the difference between earth resistance and earth electrode resistance?

Only one of the terminals is evident in the earth resistance. In order to find the second terminal we should recourse to its definition: Earth Resistance is the resistance existing between the electrically accessible part of a buried electrode and another point of the earth, which is far away.

289. The resistance of the electrode has the following components:

a. the resistance of the metal and that of the connection to it.

b. the contact resistance of the surrounding earth to the electrode.

290. What is use of lockout relay in ht voltage?

A lock-out relay is generally placed in line before or after the e-stop switch so the power can be shut off at one central location. This relay is powered by the same electrical source as the control power and is operated by a key lock switch. The relay itself may have up to 24 contact points within the unit itself. This allows the control power for multiple machines to be locked out by the turn of a single key switch.

291. What is the power factor of an alternator at no load?

At no load Synchronous Impedance of the alternator is responsible for creating angle difference. So it should be zero lagging like inductor.

292. How to determine capacitor tolerance codes?

In electronic circuits, the capacitor tolerance can be determined by a code that appears on the casing. The code is a letter that often follows a three-digit number (such as 130Z).The first two are the 1st and 2nd significant digits and the third is a multiplier code. Most of the time the last digit tells you how many zeros to write after the first two digits and these are read as Pico-Farads.

293. Why most of analog o/p devices having o/p range 4 to 20 mA and not 0 to 20 mA?

4-20 mA is a standard range used to indicate measured values for any process. The reason that 4ma is chosen instead of 0 mA is for fail safe operation .For example- a pressure instrument gives output 4mA to indicate 0 psi, up to 20 mA to indicate 100 psi, or full scale. Due to any problem in instrument (i.e) broken wire, its output reduces to 0 mA. So if range is 0-20 mA then we can differentiate whether it is due to broken wire or due to 0 psi.

294.   What Is A Stack Pointer Register, Describe Briefly.?

•   The Stack pointer is a sixteen bit register used to point at the stack.
•   In read write memory the locations at which temporary data and return addresses are stored is known as the stack.
•   In simple words stack acts like an auto decrement facility in the system.
•   The initialization of the stack top is done with the help of an instruction LXI SP.
•   In order to avoid program crashes a program should always be written at one end and initialized at the other.

295.   What is meant by knee point voltage?

Knee point voltage is calculated for electrical Current transformers and is very important factor to choose a CT. It is the voltage at which a CT gets saturated.(CT-current transformer).

296.   What is reverse power relay?

Reverse Power flow relay are used in generating station's protection. A generating stations is supposed to fed power to the grid and in case generating units are off,there is no generation in the plant then plant may take power from grid. To stop the flow of power from grid to generator we use reverse power relay.

297.   What are the advantage of free wheeling diode in a Full Wave rectifier?

It reduces the harmonics and it also reduces sparking and arching across the mechanical switch so that it reduces the voltage spike seen in a inductive load

298.   Mention The Steps In The Interrupt Driven Mode Of Data Transfer.?

The steps followed in this type of transfer are as follows:
*   The peripheral device would request for an interrupt.
*   The request acknowledgement for the transfer is issued at the end of instruction execution.
*   Now the ISS routine is initialized, The PC has the return address which is now stored in the stack.
*   Now data transfer is managed and coordinates by the ISS.
*   Again the Interrupt system is enabled and the above steps are repeated.

299.   what is the principle of motor?

Whenever a current carrying conductor is placed in an magnetic field it produce turning or twisting movement is called as torque.

300.   Types of dc generator?

DC Generators are classified into two types 1)separatly excited DC generator
2)self excited DC generator, which is further classified into; 1)series 2)shunt and 3)compound(which is further classified into cumulative and differential).

301. Which motor has high Starting Torque and Staring current DC motor, Induction motor or Synchronous motor?

DC Series motor has high starting torque. We can not start the Induction motor and Synchronous motors on load, but can not start the DC series motor without load.

302. Define stepper motor. What is the use of stepper motor?

The motor which work or act on the applied input pulse in it, is called as stepper motor. This stepper motor is under the category of synchronous motor, which often does not fully depend of complete cycle. It likes to works in either direction related to steps. for this purpose it mainly used in automation parts.

303. Write A Program That Will Store The Contents Of An Accumulator And Flag Register At Locations 2000h And 2001h.?

By making use of the Push & Pop instructions the program can be written as:
- LXISP, 4000H - this step initiates the SP at 4000h.
- PUSH PSW - the contents of the accumulator and flag are pushed into the stack.
- POP B
- MOV A, B
- STA 2000H
- MOV A, C
- STA 2001H
- HLT

304. Which type of A.C motor is used in the fan (ceiling fan, exhaust fan, padestal fan, bracket fan etc) which are find in the houses ?

Its Single Phase induction motor which mostly squirrel cage rotor and are capacitor start capacitor run.

305.   Give two basic speed control scheme of DC shunt motor?

By using flux control method:in this method a rheostat is connected across the field winding to control the field current.so by changing the current the flux produced by the field winding can be changed, and since speed is inversely proportional to flux speed can be controlled Armature control method:in this method a rheostat is connected across armature winding by varying the resistance the value of resistive drop(IaRa) can be varied, and since speed is directly proportional to Eb-IaRa the speed can be controlled.

306.   Difference between a four point starter and three point starter?

The shunt connection in four point starter is provided separately form the line where as in three point starter it is connected with line which is the drawback in three point starter.

307.   What is the difference between synchronous generator & asynchronous generator?

In simple, synchronous generator supply's both active and reactive power but asynchronous generator(induction generator) supply's only active power and observe reactive power for magnetizing. This type of generators are used in windmills.

308.   Why syn. generators are used for the production of electricity?

Synchronous machines have capability to work on different power factor (or say different imaginary power varying the field EMF. Hence syn. generators r used for the production of electricity.

309.   Why is the starting current high in a DC motor?

In DC motors, Voltage equation is V=Eb-IaRa (V = Terminal voltage, Eb = Back emf in Motor, Ia = Armature current,Ra = Aramture resistance). At starting, Eb is zero. Therefore, V=IaRa, Ia = V/Ra ,where Ra is very less like 0.01ohm.i.e, Ia will become enormously increased.

310. What are the advantages of star-delta starter with induction motor?

The main advantage of using the star delta starter is reduction of current during the starting of the motor. Starting current is reduced to 3-4 times Of current of Direct online starting.(2). Hence the starting current is reduced , the voltage drops during the starting of motor in systems are reduced.

311. Why series motor cannot be started on no-load?

Series motor cannot be started without load because of high starting torque. Series motor are used in Trains, Crane etc.

312. Mention the methods for starting an induction motor?

The different methods of starting an induction motor
• Direct Online Starter
• Star Delta Starter
• Auto Transformer Starter
• Resistance Starter
• Series Reactor Starter

313. What are Motor Generator Sets and explain the different ways the motor generator set can be used ?

Motor Generator Sets are a combination of an electrical generator and an engine mounted together to form a single piece of equipment. Motor generator set is also referred to as a genset, or more commonly, a generator The motor generator set can used in the following different ways:
1.Alternating current (AC) to direct current (DC)
2.DC to AC
3.DC at one voltage to DC at another voltage
4.AC at one frequency to AC at another harmonically-related frequency

314.   Which type of motor is used in trains, what is the rating of supply used explain Working principal?

Dc series is in the trains to get high starting torque while starting of the trains and operating voltage is 1500v dc.

315.   What are the Application of DC Motors in Thermal Power Plant?

In thermal power plants dc motors are employed for certain control and critical emergency operations which are supplied by dedicated batteries. DC motors operate as backup drives for normal ac drive systems when ac power supply to the plant is lost.

In thermal power plant, the dc motors finds applications for performing control functions such as

- Turbine governor motor
- Governor limit setting
- Motor operated rheostats
- Emergency lubrication for the turbines (main, boiler feed pumps)
- Generator (H2 oil seal).
- DC motor operated valves

DC motors employed in thermal plants are classified in to two types based on the type of application.

DC motors carrying out Control function

Dc motors carrying out Emergency function

Control functions: This category consists of the turbine governor motor, governor limiting setting, motor operated rheostats, etc. These motors are small, about 1/8 hp or less. They are operated quite infrequently for short duration.

Emergency functions: This category consists of turbine-generator emergency (lubrication) bearing oil pumps and emergency seal oil pumps. Such pumps may also be provided for steam turbine drives of feed water pumps, fans, and other large loads. The lack of lubrication during a shutdown without ac power will ruin the linings of the bearings and damage the shaft.

Hydrogen seal oil pump is provided to prevent the escaping of hydrogen (for large turbine-generators hydrogen cooling is provided for efficient cooling) from the casing by providing a tight seal with high pressure oil

316.   What are the Advantages & Disadvantages of Synchronous motors?

Advantage or Merits:

One of the major advantage of using synchronous motor is the ability to control the power factor. An over excited synchronous motor can have leading power factor and can be operated in parallel to induction motors and other lagging power factor loads thereby improving the system power factor.

In synchronous motor the speed remains constant irrespective of the loads. This characteristics helps in industrial drives where constant speed is required irrespective of the load it is driving. It also useful when the motor is required to drive another alternator to supply at a different frequency as in frequency changes.

Synchronous motors can be constructed with wider air gaps than induction motors which makes these motors mechanically more stable.

In synchronous motors electro-magnetic power varies linearly with the voltage.

Synchronous motors usually operate with higher efficiencies (more than 90%) especially in low speed and unity power factor applications compared to induction motors

Disadvantages or Demerits:

Synchronous motors requires dc excitation which must be supplied from external sources.

Synchronous motors are inherently not self starting motors and needs some arrangement for its starting and synchronizing.

The cost per kW output is generally higher than that of induction motors.

These motors cannot be used for variable speed applications as there is no possibility of speed adjustment unless the incoming supply frequency is adjusted (Variable Frequency Drives).

Synchronous motors cannot be started on load. Its starting torque is zero.

These motors have tendency to hunt.

When loading on the synchronous motor increases beyond its capability, the synchronism between rotor and stator rotating magnetic field is lost and motor comes to halt.

Collector rings and brushes are required resulting in increase in maintenance.

Synchronous motors cannot be useful for applications requiring frequent starting or high starting torques required.

317.   What Is The Difference Between A Verilog Task And A Verilog Function?

The following rules distinguish tasks from functions:

•   A function shall execute in one simulation time unit; a task can contain time-controlling statements.

•   A function cannot enable a task; a task can enable other tasks or functions.

•   A function shall have at least one input type argument and shall not have an output or inout type argument;a task can have zero or more arguments of any type.

•   A function shall return a single value; a task shall not return a value.

318.   Explain The Differences Between "direct Mapped", "fully Associative", And "set Associative" Caches ?

If each block has only one place it can appear in the cache, the cache is said to be direct mapped. The mapping is usually (block-frame address) modulo (number of blocks in cache).

If a block can be placed anywhere in the cache, the cache is said to be fully associative.

If a block can be placed in a restricted set of places in the cache, the cache is said to be set associative. A set is a group of two or more blocks in the cache. A block is first mapped onto a set, and then the block can be placed anywhere within the set. The set is usually chosen by bit selection; that is, (block-frame address) modulo (number of sets in cache). If there are n blocks in a set, the cache placement is called n-way set associative.

319.   What Is Electric Traction?

Electric traction means using the electric power for traction system (i.e. for railways,trams, trolleys etc).

Electric traction means use of the electricity for railways,trams, trolleys etc. Now a days, magnetic traction is also used for bullet trains.and basically dc motors are used for electric traction systems.

320. How Can You Start¬up The 40w Tube Lite With 230v Ac/dc Without Using Any Choke/coil?

It's possible by means of Electronic chokes,otherwise it's not possible to ionize the particles in tube light with normal voltage.

321. What is a system-on-chip (SoC)?

Application specific integrated circuits often include entire microprocessors, memory blocks including ROM, RAM, EEPROM, Flash and other large building blocks. Such an ASIC is often termed a SoC (system-on-chip).

322. Operation Carried Out In Thermal Power Stations?

The water is obtained in the boiler and the coal is burnt so that steam is obtained this steam is allowed to hit the turbine , the turbine which is coupled with the generator generates the electricity.

323. Why Link Is Provided In Neutral Of An Ac Circuit And Fuse In Phase Of Ac Circuit?

Link is provided at a Neutral common point in the circuit from which various connection are taken for the individual control circuit and so it is given in a link form to withstand high Amps. But in the case of Fuse in the Phase of AC circuit it is designed such that the fuse rating is calculated for the particular circuit (i.e load) only.So if any malfunction happen the fuse connected in the particular control circuit alone will blow off.

324. How Tube Light Circuit Is Connected And How It Works?

A choke is connected in one end of the tube light and a starter is in series with the circuit. When supply is provided ,the starter will interrupt the supply cycle of AC. Due to the sudden change of supply the chock will generate around 1000volts . This volt will capable of to break the electrons inside the tube to make electron flow. once the current passes through the tube the starter circuit will be out of part. now there is no change of supply causes choke voltage normalized and act as minimize the current.

325.   What Is Marx Circuit?

It is used with generators for charging a number of capacitor in parallel and discharging them in series.It is used when voltage required for testing is higher than the available

326.   What Is Encoder, How It Function?

An encoder is a device used to change a signal (such as a bitstream) or data into a code. The code may serve any of a number of purposes such as compressing information for transmission or storage, encrypting or adding redundancies to the input code, or translating from one code to another.
This is usually done by means of a programmed algorithm,especially if any part is digital, while most analog encoding is done with analog circuitry.

327.   What Are The Advantages Of Speed Control Using Thyristor?
Advantages :

- Fast Switching Characterstics than Mosfet, BJT, IGBT.
- Low cost.
- Higher Accurate.

328.   Why Human Body Feel Electric Shock ?? N In An electric Train During Running , We Did Nt Feel Any shock ? Why?

Unfortunately our body is a pretty good conductor of electricity, The golden rule is Current takes the lowest resistant path if you have insulation to our feet as the circuit is not complete (wearing rubber footwear which doing some repairs is advisable as our footwear is a high resistance path not much current flows through our body).The electric train is well insulated from its electrical system.

329.   What Is The Principle Of Motor?

Whenever a current carrying conductor is placed in an magnetic field it produce turning or twisting movemnt is called as torque.

330.   Why, When Birds Sit On Transmission Lines Or Current Wires Doesn't Get Shock?

Its true that if birds touch the single one line (phase or neutral) they don't get electrical shock… if birds touch 2 lines than the circuit is closed and they get electrical shock.. so if a human touch single one line(phase) then he doesn't get shock if he is in the air (not touching – standing on the ground if he is standing on the ground then touching the line (phase) he will get a shock because the ground on what we standing is like line (ground bed – like neutral)? and in the most of electric lines the neutral is grounded..so that means that human who touch the line closes the circuit between phase and neutral.

331.   What Is Meant By Armature Reaction?

The effect of armature flu to main flux is called armature reaction. The armature flux may support main flux or opposes main flux.

332.   Describe Briefly The Accumulator Register Of 8085.?

•   It is one of the most important 8 bit register of 8085
•   It is responsible for coordinating input and output to and from the microprocessor through it.
•   The primary purpose of this register is to store temporary data and for the placement of final values of arithmetic and logical operations.
•   This accumulator register is mainly used for arithmetic, logical, store and rotate operations.

333.   Which Motor Has High Starting Torque And Staring Current Dc Motor, Induction Motor Or Synchronous Motor?

DC Series motor has high starting torque. We can not start the Induction motor and Synchronous motors on load, but can not start the DC series motor without load.

334.   What Is Acsr Cable And Where We Use It?

ACSR means Aluminium conductor steel reinforced, this conductor is used in transmission & distribution.

335.   What Is Vaccum Currcuit Breaker.define With Cause And Where Be Use It Device?

A breaker is normally used to break a ciruit. while breaking the circuit, the contact terminals will be separated. At the time of seperation an air gap is formed in between the terminals. Due to existing current flow the air in the gap is ionised and results in the arc. various mediums are used to quench this arc in respective CB's. but in VCB the medium is vaccum gas. since the air in the CB is having vaccum pressure the arc formation is interrupted. VCB's can be used upto kv.

336.   What Will Happen When Power Factor Is Leading In Distribution Of Power?

If their is high power factor, i.e if the power factor is close to one:

• losses in form of heat will be reduced,
• cable becomes less bulky and easy to carry, and very cheap to afford, &
• it also reduces over heating of tranformers.

337.   What Is The One Main Difference Between Ups & Inverter ?

Uninterrupt power supply is mainly use for short time .means according to ups VA it gives backup.
ups is also two types :
• on line.
• offline.
online ups having high volt and amp for long time backup with with high dc voltage.but ups start with 2v dc with 7 amp. but inverter is startwith 2v,24,dc to 36v dc and 20amp to 80amp

battery with long time backup.

338.   Classify Interrupts On The Basis Of Signals. State Their Differences.?

On the basis of level the signals can be classified into the following types:
*   Single level interrupts
*   Multi level interrupts
*   The differences between them are as follows:
*   For single the interrupts are manages through a single ping whereas in multi they are managed by multiple pins.
*   For single level interrupts polling is essential whereas for multi level it is not necessary.
*   Single level interrupts are much slower than multi level interrupts.

339.   What Is Power Factor? Whether It Should Be High Or Low? Why?

Power factor should be high in order to get smooth operation of the system.Low power factor means losses will be more.it is the ratio of true power to apparent power. it has to be ideally 1. if it is too low then cable over heating & equipment overloading will occur.

if it is greater than 1 then load will act as capacitor and starts feeding the source and will cause tripping.(if pf is poor ex: 0.17 to meet actual power load has to draw more current(V constant),result in more losses if pf is good.

ex: 0.95 to meet actual power load has to draw less current(V constant),result in less losses).

340.   There Are A Transformer And An Induction Machine. Those Two Have The Same Supply. For Which Device The Load Current Will Be Maximum? And Why?

The motor has max load current compare to that of transformer because the motor consumes real power.. and the transformer is only producing the working flux and its not consuming.. hence the load current in the transformer is because of core loss so it is minimum.

341.   Explain The Working Principal Of The Circuit Breaker?

Circuit Breaker is one which makes or breaks the circuit.It has two contacts namely fixed contact & moving contact.under normal condition the moving contact comes in contact with fixed contact thereby forming the closed contact for the flow of current. During abnormal & faulty conditions(when current exceeds the rated value) an arc is produced between the fixed & moving contacts & thereby it forms the open circuitArc is extinguished by the Arc Quenching media like air, oil, vaccum etc

342.   How Many Types Of Colling System It Transformers?

- ONAN (oil natural,air natural).
- ONAF (oil natural,air forced).
- OFAF (oil forced,air forced).
- ODWF (oil direct,water forced).
- OFAN (oil forced,air forced).

343.   What Is The Function Of Anti ¬pumping In Circuit Breaker?

when breaker is close at one time by close push button,the anti pumping contactor prevent re close the breaker by close push button after if it already close.

344.   What Is Stepper Motor.what Is Its Uses?

Stepper motor is the electrical machine which act upon input pulse applied to it. it is one type of synchronous motor which runs in steps in either direction instead of running in complete cycle.so, in automation parts it is used.

345.   Why The Capacitors Works On Ac Only?

Generally capacitor gives infinite resistance to dc components(i.e., block the dc components). it allows the ac components to pass through

346.   What Happens If I Connect A Capacitor To A Generator Load?

Connecting a capacitor across a generator always improves power factor,but it will help depends up on the engine capacity of the alternator,other wise the alternator will be over loaded due to the extra watts consumed due to the improvement on pf. Secondly, don't connect a capacitor across an alternator while it is picking up or without any other load.

347.   What Is The Difference Between Surge Arrestor And Lightning Arrestor?

LA is installed outside and the effect of lightning is grounded,where as surge arrestor installed inside panels comprising of resistors which consumes the energy and nullify the effect of surge.

348.   Why Use The Vcb At High Transmission System ? Why Can't Use Acb?

Actually the thing is vacuum has high arc queching property compare to air because in VCB ,the die electric strengths equal to 8 times of air . That is y always vaccum used as in HT breaker and air used as in LT .

349.   Difference Between A Four Point Starter And Three Point Starter?

The shunt connection in four point stater is provided separately form the line where as in three point stater it is connected with line which is the drawback in three point stater.

350.   What Is An Exciter And How Does It Work?

There are two types of exciters, static exciter and rotory exciter.
purpose of excitor is to supply the excitation dc voltage to the fixed poles of generator.
Rotory excitor is an additional small generator mounted on the shaft of main generator. if it is dc generator, it will supply dc to the rotory poles through slip ring and brushes(conventional alternator).
If it is an ac excitor, out put of ac excitor is rectified by rotating diodes and supply dc to main fixed poles.ac excitor is the ac generator whose field winding are stationary and armature rotates. initial voltage is built up by residual magnetism.It gives the starting torque to the generator.

351. What Is Automatic Voltage Regulator(avr)?

AVR is an abbreviation for Automatic Voltage Regulator.It is important part in Synchronous Generators, it controls theoutput voltage of the generator by controlling its excitation current. Thus it can control the output Reactive Power of the Generator.

352. Enlist Types Of Dc Generator?

D.C.Generators are classified into two types:
- separatly exicted d.c.generator.
- self exicted d.c.generator.
which is further classified into;1)series 2)shunt and compound(which is further classified into cumulative and differential).

353. Why Syn. Generators Are Used For The Production Of Electricity?

Synchronous machines have capability to work on different power factor(or say different imaginary pow varying the field emf. Hence syn. generators are used for the production of electricity.

354. What Is The Difference Between Synchronous Generator & Asynchronous Generator?

In simple, synchronous generator supply's both active and reactive power but asynchronous generator(induction generator) supply's only active power and observe reactive power for magnetizing.This type of generators are used in windmills.

355. What Is Boucholz Relay And The Significance Of It In To The Transformer?

Boucholz relay is a device which is used for the protection of transformer from its internal faults, it is a gas based relay. whenever any internal fault occurs in a transformer, the boucholz relay at once gives a horn for some time, if the transformer is isolated from the circuit then it stop its sound itself other wise it trips the circuit by its own tripping mechanism.

356.   What Are The Two Major Differences Between Intr And Other Interrupts (Hardware)?

The two major differences between INTR and the other hardware interrupts are as follows:
•   All the hardware interrupts are vectored interrupts but the INTR interrupt is not so. An INTR interrupt will always get the address of a subroutine from the device (external) itself. In the case of other hardware interrupts the interrupts come from the call generated by the processor at a already determined vector location.
•   In case of the INTR interrupt the return address of an interrupt is never saved but in the case of other hardware interrupts the locations is saved in the stack.

357.   Explain Briefly The Trap Input For The 8085.?

•   The TRAP input is sensitive to both edge and level.
•   The pulse width for this signal should be in excess as compared to the normal noise width.
•   A second trap will never be able to respond for the second time as it requires the first trap to go through a high to low transition.
•   The pulse widths are wider than normal widths so as to prevent unwanted false triggers..

358.   What Is Meant By Insulation Voltage In Cables? Explain It?

It is the property of a cable by virtue of it can withstand the applied voltage without rupturing it is known as insulation level of the cable.

359.   What Are The Advantages Of Star¬ Delta Starter With Induction Motor?

Resolution:

- The main advantage of using the star delta starter is reduction of current during the starting of the motor.Starting current is reduced to 3⁻4 times Of current of Direct online starting.

- Hence the starting current is reduced , the voltage drops during the starting of motor in systems are reduced.

360.   Why Delta Star Transformers Are Used For Lighting Loads?

For lighting loads, neutral conductor is must and hence the secondary must be star winding. and this lighting load is always unbalanced in all three phases. To minimize the current unbalance in the primary we use delta winding in the primary. So delta / star transformer is used for lighting loads.

361.   What Is Meant By Regenerative Braking?

When the supply is cutt off for a running motor, it still continue running due to inertia. In order to stop it quickly we place a load(resitor) across the armature winding and the motor should have maintained continuous field supply. so that back e.m.f voltage is made to apply across the resistor and due to load the motor stops quickly.This type of breaking is called as "Regenerative Breaking".

Define luminous flux

It is defined as the total quantity of light energy emitted per second from a luminous body.

It is represented by symbol F and is measured in lumens.

The conception of luminous flux helps us to specify the output and efficiency of a given light source.

362.   What is meant by luminance?

It is defined as the luminous per unit projected area of either a surface source of light or a reflecting surface and is denoted by L.

363.   What are the laws of illumination?

Law of Inverse squares

Illumination at a point is inversely proportional to square of its distance from the point source and directly proportional to the luminous

intensity (CP) of the source of light in that direction.

If a source of light which emits light equally in all directions be placed at the centre of a hollow sphere, the light will fall uniformly on

the inner surface of the sphere.

If the sphere be replaced by one of the larger radius, the same total amount of light is spread over a larger area proportional to the square

of the radius.

Lamber's cosine law:

The illumination at a point on a surface is proportional to cosine of the angle which ray makes with the normal to the normal to the surface at

that point.

364.   What is meant by candle power?

It is defined as the number of lumens given out by the source in a unit solid angle in a given direction.

It is denoted by CP

Cp = lumens /?

365.   Define MHCP

The mean of candle power in all directions in the horizontal plane containing the source of light is termed as Mean Horizontal Candle Power

366.   What are all the sources of light?

As per the principle of operation the light sources may be grouped as follows

• Arc lamps

• High temperature Lamps

• Gaseous Discharge Lamps

- Fluorescent type Lamps

367. Define utilisation factor

It is defined as the ratio of total lumens reaching the working plane to total lumens given out by the lamp utilisation factor = Total lumens reaching the working plane. / Total lumens given out by the lamp.

368. Name the various photometer heads

- Bunsen head or Grease spot photometer
- Lummer-brodhun photometer head
- There are two types of lummer broadhun heads
- Equality oc Brightness type photometer head
- Contrast type photometer head

369. What is polar curve?

In most lamps or sources of light the luminous intensity is not the same in all directions.
If the luminous intensity, ie, the candle power is measured in a horizontal plane about a vertical axis and a curve is plotter between candle power and the angular position, a curve obtained is called as horizontal polar curve.
The luminous intensity in all the directions can be represented by polar curves.
If the luminous intensity in a vertical plane is plotted against position, a curve known as vertical polar curve.

370. Define space-height ratio

It is defined as the ratio of horizontal distance between adjacent lamps and height of their mountings.
Space-height ratio = Horizontal distance between two adjacent lamps. / Mounting height of lamps above working plane.

371.   Define Power and Energy?

The rate at which work is done in an electric circuit is known as Electric power.
Power = Voltage X Current
The basic unit for electric power is Watts
The instrument used to measure the power is known as watt meter.The total amount of work
done in an electric circuit is called as electric
energy.
Energy = Power X Time
the basic unit is Joule or watt-sec
The practical unit is Kilo watt-hour
The instrument used to measure the energy is known as Energy meter.

372.   In our house are we monitoring/measuring power or energy?

Energy. It is done by energy meter.

373.   what is meant by cycle in ac waveform? what is period? Define frequency?

One complete set of change in value is known as waveform.
If you any basic question on AC waveform, then first draw an ac waveform and explain with
reference to the waveform.

374.   Explain about various AC Values?

Instantaneous value: Instantaneous values are the values of the alternating quantities at any
instant of time. They are represented by smallletters like i, e etc.
Peak value: The largest value reached in a half cycle is called the peak value or the maximum
value or the amplitude of the waveform. Such values are represented by Vm, Im etc.
Peak-to-peak value is the difference between the maximum and minimum values in a cycle.
Average value: The average or mean value of a symmetrical alternating quantity (such as a
sine wave), is the average value measured over a half cycle (since over a complete cycle the
average value is zero). For a sine wave, average value = 0.637 times maximum value
RMS Value: The effective value of an alternating current is that current which will produce

the same heating effect as an equivalent direct current. The effective value is called the root mean square (rms) value and whenever an alternating quantity is given, it is assumed to be the rms value.

375.   What is form factor and peak factor?

The ratio of rms value to average value of an ac quantity is called form factor.
Form Factor = RMS value/ Average value
The ratio of maximum value to the RMS value of an ac quantity is called as peak factor.
Peak Factor = Maximum Value/RMS value

376. What type of architecture used in 8085 microprocessor?

8085 has Von Neumann architecture. It is named after the mathematician John   Von Neumann. It is based on the concept of stored program control. In this architecture both the data and the program is stored in the same memory.

377. What is the function of accumulator?

Accumulator is an 8 bit register which stores data and performs arithmetic and logical operations. The result of the operation is stored in the accumulator. It is designated by the letter 'A'.

378. What are the different types of flags in 8085 microprocessor?

There are 5 different flags in 8085 microprocessor. Though the flag register is of 8 bit but 3 bits are not in use. Only 5 bits are used for the different flags. They are:-
a) Sign flag(s)– This is designated by the letter 'S'. If sign bit is 1 then the sign flag is set to 1 and if the sign bit is zero then sign flag is reset to zero.
b) Zero flag(z)– This is designated by the letter 'z'. If the result of any arithmetic or logical operation is zero i.e. all the bits are zero then zero flag is set to 1 else it is set to zero.
c) Auxiliary carry– (AC) This flag is set to 1 only when any intermediate carry is produced. Else it is reset to 0.

d) Parity flag (P) – when the result of any operation has odd number of ones then parity flag is set to 1 else if it has even number of ones then it is reset to 0.

e) Carry flag(C) – this flag is set to 1 only when a carry is produced in the result i.e. the carry bit is 1 else if the carry bit is zero then the flag is reset to zero.

379. What are the types of general purpose registers in 8085?

There are 6 general purpose registers in 8085 microprocessor. They are designated by the letters – B, C, D, E, H, and L. These are 8 bit registers and are used to store data temporarily during the execution of any program. These registers can also be used to store 16 bit data by using them in pairs i.e. BC, DE and HL. These pairs cannot be changed as B cannot pair with any other register other than C.

380. What is the length of stack pointer in 8085 microprocessor? And what is its use?

stack pointer is of 16 bits length and is used to point to the value at top of the stack for the currently executed instruction.

381. What is the memory size of 8085 microprocessor?

8085 has 8 data lines and 16 address lines. The memory size of any microprocessor depends on the number of address lines. The general formula is 2^n, where n= number of address lines. For 8085 there are 2^{16}= 64 Kbytes memory size.

382. How many bits is 8085 microprocessor?

Microprocessor is named on the basis of number of data lines in it. 8085 is a bit microprocessor as it has 8 bit data lines.

383. What are the various interrupts in 8085 microprocessor? Which is the highest priority interrupt?

There are 6 types of interrupts in 8085. They are
a) TRAP

b) RST 7.5

c) RST 6.5

d) RST 5.5

e) INTR

f) Interrupt acknowledgment (INTA(bar)).

TRAP has the highest priority among all the interrupts.

384. Which type of cycle is used for fetch and execute instruction?

Instruction cycle is used for the fetch and execute instruction.

In this cycle the instruction is fetched, decoded and executed to produce the required output.

385. How many address lines are there in 8085 microprocessor?

There are 16 address lines in 8085. They are multiplexed address and data lines. Address bus of 8085 is of 16 bits. During the first machine cycle these address lines are used as data lines and in the next machine cycle all the 16 lines act as address lines.

The multiplexed 8 address and data lines refer to lower order address bit and the rest 8 for higher order address bits.

386. What is a Microprocessor?

Microprocessor is a program-controlled device, that fetches the instructions from memory, decode it & executes the instructions. Generally Microprocessor are single- chip devices.

387. Why crystal is being preferred as a clock source?

Reasons-high stability, large Q (Quality Factor) & the frequency that doesn't drift with aging. so crystal is used as a clock source most of the times.

388. Name High order / Low order Register in 8085 microprocessor?

Flag is called Low order register & Accumulator is called High order Register in 8085 microprocessor.

389. Describe Tri-state logic?

Three Logic Levels are used and they are known as High, Low, High impedance state. The high and low are said to be normal logic levels where as high impedance state is electrical open circuit conditions. Tri-state logic has a enable line as third line

390. What will happen if HLT instruction is executed in processor?

The Micro Processor will enter into Halt-State and the buses will be tri-stated.

391. Which Stack is used in 8085?

LIFO (Last In First Out) stack is used in 8085.In this type of Stack the information which is stored last will be taken out or retrieved first.

392. Describe briefly Program counter?

Program counter does either of the two things that is it holds the address of either the first byte of the next instruction to be fetched for execution or the address of the next byte of a multi byte instruction, which was not completely fetched. In both the cases it is incremented automatically one by one as the instruction bytes will be fetched. Program register also keeps the next instruction address.

393. Name the 1st / 2nd / 3rd / 4th generation processor?

The processor are made of PMOS / NMOS / HMOS / HCMOS technology which is called 1st / 2nd / 3rd / 4th generation processor, and that is made up of 4 / 8 / 16 / 32 bits respectively.

394. Name the processor lines of two major manufacturers?

The Processor lines names of two major manufacturers are as follows:- At High-end: Intel – Pentium (II, III, IV), AMD – Athlon. At Low-end: Intel – Celeron, AMD – Duron. 64-bit: Intel – Itanium 2, AMD – Opteron

395. Mention the speed and device maximum specs for Firewire?

IEEE 1394 (Firewire) with speeds up to 400 Mbps can support the maximum of 63 connected devices

396. Where's MBR located on the disk?

The place where MBR is situated is in sector 0, track 0, head 0, cylinder 0 of the primary active partition.

397. Where does CPU Enhanced mode originate from?

Intel's 80386 was the first 32-bit processor, and so the company had to backward-support the 8086. All the modern Intel-based processors run in the enhanced mode which are capable to switch in between real mode and protected mode, which is the current mode of operation.

398. What are the types of buses?

Three types of buses are there:-
Address bus: It carries the Address to the memory to fetch either instruction..
Data bus : It carries data from the memory.
Control bus : It carries the control signals like RD/WR, Select etc.

399. What does EU do?

Execution Unit receives both program instruction codes & data from Bus Interface Unit and then executes these instructions and the result is being stored in registers.
25) Mention RST for the TRAP?
RST 4.5

400. Can an RC circuit be used as clock source for 8085?

Yes,RC circuit can be used as clock source if in case an accurate clock frequency is not required. The cost of RC is low as compared to LC.

Microprocessor interview on 8086

401. What are the types of flags in 8086?

In 8086 there are 9 types of flags which are as follows Carry flag, Parity flag, Auxiliary carry flag, Zero flag, Overflow flag, Trace flag, Interrupt flag, Direction flag, and Sign flag.

402. What are the various interrupts in 8086?

Two types of interrupts:-Maskable interrupts, Non-Maskable interrupts.

403. What is meant by Maskable interrupts?

An interrupt that can be turned off by the programmer is known as Maskable interrupts are those interrupts which can be turned off by the programmer or can be ignored by the programmer.

404. What is Non-Maskable interrupts?

A processor interrupt which can be never be turned off (i.e.disabled) or cannot be ignored by the programmer is known as Non-Maskable interrupt.

405. Which interrupts are generally used for critical events?

Non-Maskable interrupts are generally used in critical events. For example- Power failure, Emergency, Shut off etc.

406. Give some examples for Maskable interrupts?

Some examples for maskable interrupts are as follows:- RST 7.5, RST6.5, RST5.5

407. Give some example for Non-Maskable interrupts?

Trap is called as Non-Maskable interrupts, which is used during emergency condition

408. What is the Maximum clock frequency in 8086?

5 Mhz

409. Name the various segment registers in 8086?

The various segment registers in 8085 are- Code, Data, Stack, Extra Segment registers.

410. Which Stack is used in 8086?

FIFO (First In First Out) stack is used in 8086.In this type of Stack the information which is stored first is taken out or retrieved first.

411. What is SIM and RIM instructions?

SIM is Set Interrupt Mask. which is used to mask the hardware interrupts. RIM is Read Interrupt Mask which is used to check whether the interrupt is masked or not.

412. Which is the tool which is used to connect the user and the computer?

Interpreter

413. What is the position of the Stack Pointer after the PUSH instruction?

The address line is 02 less than the earlier value.

414. What is the position of the Stack Pointer after the POP instruction?

The address line is 02 greater than the earlier value.

415. What is 8051 Microcontroller ?

The Intel 8051 microcontroller is one of the most popular general-purpose microcontrollers in use today. It is an 8-bit family of microcontroller developed by Intel in the year 1981. This microcontroller was also referred to as "system on a chip" because it has 128 bytes of RAM, 4Kbytes of ROM, 2 Timers, 1 Serial port, and four ports on a single chip. 8051 microcontroller allows CPU to work on 8bits of data at a time.n case the data is larger than 8 bits then it has to be broken into parts so that the CPU can process conveniently.

416. What are registers in Microcontroller ?

Register provides a fast way to collect and store data using microcontrollers and processors.If we want to manipulate data with a controller or processor by performing tasks like addition, subtraction, and so on, we cannot do that directly in the memory, in order to perform these tasks we need registers to process and store the data. Microcontrollers contain several types of registers that can be classified according to their content or instructions that operate on them.

The 8051 microcontroller contains mainly two types of registers:

•   General purpose registers (Byte addressable registers)

•   Special function registers (Bit addressable registers)

The 8051 microcontroller consists of 256 bytes of RAM memory, which is divided into two ways, such as 128 bytes for general purpose and 128 bytes for special function registers (SFR) memory. The memory which is used for general purpose is called as RAM memory, and the memory used for SFR contains all the peripheral related registers like Accumulator, 'B' register, Timers or Counters, and interrupt related registers.

417. List Interrupts available in 8051 Microcontroller

•   External interrupt 0 (IE0) has highest priority among interrupts.

•   Timer interrupt 0 (TF0)

•   External interrupt 1 (IE1)

•   Timer interrupt 1 (TF1) has lowest priority among other interrupts.

•   Serial port Interrupt

•   Reset

418. What is stack pointer in 8051 Microcontroller?

In 8051 a stack pointer is 8 bits wide register to access stack.The stack is a section of RAM used by the CPU to store information temporarily information could be data or an address. Generally, 8051 used bank1 of internal RAM as the stack so the default stack pointer is 07H.The stack is used for PUSH, POP, CALL, RET instructions and work on the principle of last in first output (LIFO)

419. List some features of 8051 Microcontroller.

Below are the some features of 8051 Microcontroller.
- 64K bytes on-chip program memory (ROM)
- 128 bytes on-chip data memory (RAM)
- Four register banks
- 128 user defined software flags
- 8-bit bidirectional data bus
- 16-bit unidirectional address bus
- 32 general purpose registers each of 8-bit
- 16 bit Timers (usually 2, but may have more or less)
- Three internal and two external Interrupts
- Four 8-bit ports,(short model have two 8-bit ports)
- 16-bit program counter and data pointer

420. What is an Interrupt service routine in Microcontroller?

When Microcontroller is under sudden interrupt, it will call ISR (Interrupt service routine) that will store the address of current memory address and takes the control to new interrupt memory address. After the interrupt, the control will transfer back to its previous address.

421. What is an interrupt? List various types of interrupts available in 8051 Microcontroller?

Interrupt: An interrupt is a signal to the processor emitted by hardware or software indicating an event that needs immediate attention. An interrupt alerts the processor to a high-priority condition requiring the interruption of the current code the processor is executing.The processor responds by suspending its current activities, saving its state, and executing a function called an interrupt handler (or an interrupt service routine, ISR) to deal with the event. This interruption is temporary, and, after the interrupt handler finishes, the processor resumes normal activities.There are two types of interrupts: hardware interrupts and software interrupts.(source: https://en.wikipedia.org/wiki/Interrupt)

422. Explain architecture of 8051 Microcontroller?

8051 Microcontroller is based on Harvard Architecture and developed primarily for use in embedded systems technology.Its architecture consists of following units
- Central Processor Unit (CPU)
- Interrupts
- Memory
- BUS
- Oscillator
- Input/Output Port
- Timers/Counters

423. What is Address Bus, Data Bus and Control Bus in Microprocessor 8051 ?

Address Bus: Address Bus is used for address memory locations and to transfer the address from CPU to Memory of the microcontroller.Microcontroller 8051 has a 16 bit address bus for transferring the data.8051 have four addressing modes they are
- Immediate addressing modes.
- Bank address (or) Register addressing mode.
- Direct Addressing mode.
- Register indirect addressing mode.

Data Bus:Data Bus is used to transfer data within Microprocessor and Memory/Input or Output devices. It is bi-directional as Microprocessor requires to send or receive data. The data bus also works as address bus when multiplexed with lower order address bus. 8051 has 8 bits of the data bus, which is used to carry data of particular applications

Control Bus:Control bus manages the information flow between components indicating whether the operation is a read or a write and ensuring that the operation happens at the right time.

424. Which interrupt has highest priority in Microcontroller ?

Trap interrupt has the highest priority.A trap is an abnormal condition detected by the CPU, which indicates an unknown I/O device is accessed, etc

425. List some 8051 Microcontroller applications in embedded systems ?

The applications of 8051 Microcontroller is involved in 8051 based projects. Below are the list of 8051 projects .
- Arduino Managed High Sensitive based Power Saver for Street Light Control System
- The Temperature Humidity Monitoring System of Soil Based on Wireless Sensor Networks using Arduino
- RFID based Electronic Passport System for Easy Governance using Arduino
- Arduino based RFID Sensed Device Access
- Arduino based DC Motor Speed Control
- Arduino Based Line Following Robot
- Zigbee based Automatic Meter Reading System
- GSM based Electricity Energy Meter Billing with Onsite Display
- Android Phone Speech Recognition Sensed Voice Command based Notice Board Display
- Parking Availability Indication System
- Voice Controlled Home Appliances
- Remote Control Home Appliances
- PC Mouse operated Electrical Load Control Using VB Application
- Solar Highway Lighting System with Auto Turn Off in Daytime
- 8051 Microcontroller based Wireless Energy Meter
- Farmer Friendly Solar Based Electric Fence for Deterring Cattles
- Vehicle Movement Sensed Streetlight with Daytime auto off Features

426. What are applications of 8051 microcontrollers?

The constant growth in information technology has provided many benefits of making use of a microcontroller, integrated circuits, embedded chips, microprocessors, etc. With these technologies, work is done faster and complexity is reduced. The 88051 microcontrollers are used in electronic and electrical circuits. You can also find its application in robotics and artificial intelligence.

427. What is the difference between microprocessor and microcontroller?

Microprocessor differs from microcontrollers in different areas. Based on external peripheral, storage locations like ROM (Read-only memory), RAM (Random access memory) and EEPROM are embedded in microcontroller while external circuits are used in the microprocessor. Every peripheral is on one chip but they are bulky in the microprocessor. The microcontroller is less expensive than microprocessors and devices manufactured with microprocessors are cheaper too because of the metal oxide semiconductor technology used. Microprocessors are faster than microcontrollers.

428. What is a PIC microcontroller?

PIC microcontrollers (Programmable Interface Controllers Microcontrollers) are programmable circuits that perform many functions. Pic microcontroller can be programmed to function as a timer, production line controller and other tasks. You can see programmable interface controllers in applications such as computer control systems, electronic phones, alarm systems, and every other electronic device. PIC controllers exist in different types though ones found in the GENIE range are considered as the best and they are cheap to buy.

429. What is the use of PIC microcontroller?

There are different uses of the programmable interface controller. Some of the applications are video games, peripherals, audio accessories and many more. Since this circuit is programmable, it can be used for many functions like timer and to control the production line.

430. What is ARM microcontroller?

The ARM microcontroller is considered by many as the most popular microcontroller existing in the world of the digital embedded system. Many industries prefer to make use of

ARM microcontrollers because of the many exciting features. With ARM microcontroller, such industries can easily implement high performing products. The ARM microcontroller is cost-sensitive and its applications range to sensors, wireless networking, automotive body system, and others.

431. Where ARM chips are used?

Arm processors or chips are used in different electronic applications or devices. Devices, where the ARM chips are used, include tablets, multimedia players, smartphones, wearables, and other mobile devices. Arm chips need little transistors because of their instruction set. The use of ARM chips to the devices mentioned above and those not mentioned will keep on increasing because of the small size, little consumable power, and reduced complexity.

432. List some 8051 microcontroller interrupts?

There are 5 major sources of interrupt an 8051 microcontroller passes through. An interrupt is when the microprocessor stops its operation on a present task to look for signals from another task. It performs its operation on the new task before going back to the first task. The 8051 microcontroller interrupts are:
- TF0 which stands for Timer 0 overflow interrupt
- TFI which stands for Timer 1 overflow interrupt
- INT0 or External hardware interrupt
- Int1 or External hardware interrupt
- Serial communication interrupt- RI/TI

433. List some microcontroller examples?

There are many examples of the microcontroller. Some of the examples are Altera, Atmel, Espressif system, ELAN microelectronics Corp., Maxim Integrated, Cypress Semiconductor, Analog Devices, Intel, Holtek, National Semiconductor, NEC, Freescale Semiconductor, Fujitsu, Panasonic, Microchip technology, Hyperstone, Infineon, Parallax, Nuvoton technology, Sony, Toshiba, Spansion, Rockwell, XMOS, Rabbit semiconductor, Silicon Motion, Redpine signals, Ubicom, Sortable table and many more.

434. What is a data pointer in 8051 Microcontrollers?

Data pointer in the 8051 microcontrollers is one of the storage registers. Other storage registers in an 8051 microcontroller are the accumulator, the stack pointer (SP), R register, B register and the program counter (PC). The Data Pointer in 8051 microcontrollers in short form DPTR is the only 2-byte register a user can access. Other registers like the B register and accumulator are 1-byte register. This data pointer just like the name implies is for data pointing. With it, the 8051 can access memory outside the system.

435. What is embedded Microcontroller?

A microcontroller is an integrated circuit that governs one particular task in an embedded system. Every typical microcontroller has a memory, a processor and input and output peripheral all on a single chip. In some cases, it is called an embedded controller and it is used in vending machines, vehicles, medical devices, home appliances, robots, and mobile radio transceivers. They are small personal computers used for controlling small features of a bigger component.

436. List major components of microcontroller?

A microcontroller has many components. Some of the major components of a microcontroller are Central processing unit(CPU), Input and output ports, Digital analog converters, Random Access Memory)(RAM), Serial interfacing ports, Read-Only Memory(ROM), Oscillatory circuits, interrupt controls, Timers and Counters and Analog to digital converters. Every microcontroller has one or more of the components mentioned above.

437. What are different types of Microcontrollers?

There are different types of microcontrollers. They include:
• PIC Microcontroller: PIC microcontroller stands for a programmable interface controller used for developing computer robotics, electronics, and similar devices. The PIC controller is made up of data bus, dedicated processor and built-in data memory that plays a role in preparing input and output methods

- ARM Microcontroller: It is more popular than other microcontrollers. The ARM means Advanced RISC Machine and widely used by industries because of its unique features. Sensor and wireless networks are some of the devices produced with ARM microcontrollers.
- 8051 Microcontroller: This is another type of microcontroller develops by Intel in the year 1981. It has 40 pins and four programmable parallel 8-bit ports.
- AVR Microcontroller: AVR microcontroller is an advanced Harvard architecture machine. The AVR in full form is Alf and Vegard's RISC Processor.
- MSP Microcontroller: The mixed-signal processor is another type of microcontroller from the Texas instruments family. It is cost-effective and gives a good performance in the denser programming code.

438. What Are The Various Registers In 8085?

Accumulator register, Temporary register, Instruction register, Stack Pointer, Program Counter are the various registers in 8085.

439. What Are The Various Flags Used In 8085?

Sign flag, Zero flag, Auxillary flag, Parity flag, Carry flag.

440. What Is Stack Pointer?

Stack pointer is a special purpose 16-bit register in the Microprocessor, which holds the address of the top of the stack.

441. What Is Program Counter?

Program counter holds the address of either the first byte of the next instruction to be fetched for execution or the address of the next byte of a multi byte instruction, which has not been completely fetched.In both the cases it gets incremented automatically one by one as the instruction bytes get fetched. Also Program register keeps the address of the next instruction. Assembly Programming Tutorial

442. Which Stack Is Used In 8085?

LIFO (Last In First Out) stack is used in 8085.In this type of Stack the last stored information can be retrieved first.

443. What Happens When Hlt Instruction Is Executed In Processor?

The Micro Processor enters into Halt-State and the buses are tri-stated.

444. What Is Meant By A Bus?

A bus is a group of conducting lines that carriers data, address, & control signals.

445. What Is Tri-state Logic?

Three Logic Levels are used and they are High, Low, High impedance state. The high and low are normal logic levels & high impedance state is electrical open circuit conditions. Tri-state logic has a third line called enable line.

446. Give An Example Of One Address Microprocessor?

8085 is a one address microprocessor.

447. In What Way Interrupts Are Classified In 8085?

In 8085 the interrupts are classified as Hardware and Software interrupts.

448. What Are Hardware Interrupts?

TRAP, RST7.5, RST6.5, RST5.5, INTR.

449. What Are Software Interrupts?

RST0, RST1, RST2, RST3, RST4, RST5, RST6, RST7.

450. Which Interrupt Has The Highest Priority?

TRAP has the highest priority.

ASSIGNMENT QUESTIONS FOR SELF PREPARATION
FOR INTERVIEW

1. What is your background?
2. Why did you decide to become an electrical engineer?
3. What are your strengths and weaknesses?
4. What are your short term and long term goals?
5. What motivates you to succeed?
6. What do you think separates you from other candidates?
7. What electrical engineering computer software are you comfortable with?
8. Where did you get your electrical engineering degree and which classes did you excel in?
9. What qualities do you have that would be helpful on this job?
10. What is your specialty within electrical engineering?
11. Describe a challenge that you ran into at work and how you solved it.
12. Tell me about a time when you made a mistake. How did you recover?
13. Describe your most successful teamwork experience. What made it so successful?
14. Describe a time when you had to meet a strict deadline. How did you manage to get your work done on time?
15. What was the toughest decision that you've had to make within this last year?
16. Explain some of the projects that you have helped design. How did your involvement affect the outcome?
17. Tell me about a time you had to raise an uncomfortable issue with your boss.
18. How do you prioritize when in charge of multiple projects or tasks?
19. Have you ever had to make an important decision quickly? What was the outcome?
20. Tell me about a time when you went above and beyond to get the job done. Did you face any challenges along the way?
21. Can you explain the difference between direct and alternating current?
22. Explain Norton's Theorem in a single sentence.
23. What are some of the most common causes of transformer humming?
24. What is the difference between a single pole and a double pole circuit breaker?
25. A capacitor has a label on it saying, "100 WVDC". What does this label mean and what is the consequence of exceeding this rating?

26. What is the difference between generator and alternator?

27. What is your understanding of Australian engineering standard 61508?

28. What is analog-to-digital conversion of signals?

29. What are the various types of numbers for network identity?

30. A client is using Chlorine gas as a sanitiser. However, the facility is only 300m from a public area and poses a significant risk. What decision making process would you take the client through to remove the risk?

REFERENCES

1. A Textbook Of Electrical Technology : Basic Electrical Engineering In S. I.Units (Volume-1) By B.L. Theraja,A.K. Theraja

2. A Textbook Of Electrical Technology Volume – III (Transmission,Distribution And Utilization) By B.L. Theraja,A.K. Theraja

3. A Textbook Of Electrical Technology Volume – IV (Electronic Devices AndCircuits) By B.L. Theraja,A.K. Theraja

4. Electrical Engineering: Principles & Applications By Allan R. Hambley

5. Basic Engineering Circuit Analysis By J. David Irwin, R. Mark Nelms

6. Basic Electronics For Scientists And Engineers By Dennis L. Eggleston

7. Teach Yourself Electricity And Electronics By Stan Gibilisco, Simon Monk

8. Basic Electrical Engineering By D C Kulshreshtha

9. A First Course On Electrical Drives By S.K. Pillai

10. Circuit Theory By A.V.Bakshi, U.A.Bakshi

11. Electronic Devices And Circuits By K. Lal Kishore

12. Electronics – From Theory Into Practice: Applied Electricity And Electronics Division By J. E. Fisher, H. B. Gatland

13. Electronic Devices And Amplifier Circuits With Matlab Applications BySteven T. Karris

14. Electronic Devices (Conventional Current Version) By Thomas L. Floyd

15. Electronic Devices And Circuit Theory By Robert L Boylestad And LouisNashelsky

16. Electronics Engineering By A.P.Godse, U.A.Bakshi

17. Make: Electronics (Learning By Discovery) By Charles Platt

18. Operational Amplifiers By G B Clayton,Steve Winder

19. Operational Amplifiers: Theory And Design By Johan Huijsing

20. Electronic Circuits For The Evil Genius By Dave Cutcher

21. Basic Electrical Engineering By U.A. Bakshi, V.U. Bakshi

22. Basic Electrical Engineering By C L Wadhwa

23. Basic Electrical Engineering By V.K Mehta,Rohit Mehta

24. Basic Electrical Engineering By Abhijit Chakrabarti, Sudipta Nath, ChandanChanda

25. Handbook Of Electrical Installation Practice By Geoffrey Stokes

26. A Textbook Of Electrical Technology By R.K. Rajput

27.   Fundamentals Of Electrical Engineering By Giorgio Rizzoni

28.   Elements Of Electrical Engineering By U.A.Bakshi, V.U.Bakshi

29.   Basic Electrical Engineering By Dr. D P Kothari, Prof I J Nagrath

30.   Basic Concepts Of Electrical Engineering By Kuldeep Sahay, ShivendraPathak

31.   Basic Electrical Technology By Iit Kharagpur

32.   V.N. Mittle "Basic Electrical Engineering", Tata McGraw Hill Edition, New Delhi, 1990.

33.   R.S. Sedha, "Applied Electronics" S. Chand & Co., 2006.

34.   Electrical Technology by Surinder Pal Bali, Pearson Publications.

35.   Electronic Devices and Circuits, R.L. Boylestad and Louis Nashelsky, 9th edition, PEI/PHI 2006.

36.   Fundamentals of Electrical Circuits by Charles k.Alexander, Mattew N.O.Saidiku, Tata McGraw Hill company.

37.   Muthusubramanian R, Salivahanan S and Muraleedharan K A, "Basic Electrical, Electronics, and Computer Engineering" , Tata McGraw Hill, Second Edition, (2006).

38.   Nagsarkar T K and Sukhija MS, "Basics of Electrical Engineering", Oxford Press (2005).

39.   Mehta V K, "Principles of Electronics", S.Chand & Company Ltd, (1994).

40.   Mahmood Nahvi and Joseph A. Edminister, "Electric Circuits", Schaum' Outline Series, McGraw Hill, (2002).

41.   Premkumar N, "Basic Electrical Engineering", Anuradha Publishers, (2003).

42.   Circuit theory(Analysis and Synthesis) by A. Chakrabarti-Dhanpat Rai&Co.

43.   Network Theory by Prof.B.N.Yoganarasimham.

44.   Circuit Theory by Sudhakar and Shyam Mohan.

45.   Electrical Machines-I by B.I.Theraja

46.   Electrical Circuit Theory and Technology by John Bird, Routledge Taylor &Francis Group

47.   Basic Electrical Engineering by M.S.Naidu and S.Kamakshiah, TMH Publications

48.   Fundamentals of Electrical Engineering by Rajendra Prasad, PHI Publications,2nd edition

49.   Basic Electrical Engineering by Nagsarkar, Sukhija, Oxford Publications,2nd edition

50.   Industrial Electronics by G.K. Mittal, PHI

51.   Textbook of Basic Electrical Engineering –TMH Publishing Co.

52. A. Patel, Textbook of Elements of Electrical Engineering, Mahajan Publishing House, Ahmedabad.

53. Nagrath, Basic Electrical Engineering, TMH Publishing Co. Ltd.

54. Vincent Del Toro, Textbook of Principles of Electrical Engg., Prentice Hall of India Pvt. Ltd., New Delhi.

55. S. Samaddar, Textbook of Electric Wiring, New Central Book Agency (P) Ltd., Calcutta.

56. Surjit Singh, Textbook of Electrical Design Estimating and Costing, Dhanpat Rai & Sons.

57. Robert Boylestad, Louis Mashlsky, Electronics Devices and Circuit theory, Peerson

58. Morris Mano, Digital logic and computer Design, PHI

59. Network Analysis......Van Valken Burg

60. Solutions of Network Analysis........GK Publications

61. Engg. Circuit Analysis........ Hayt and Kemmerly

62. Network Analysis.... Soni and Gupta

63. Graph Theory......... Narsing Deo (Cutset and Others)

64. Circuit Theory.........Chakravarthy

65. Circuit Theory.........Roy Choudary (Networks and Systems)

66. Electric Circuits....... Schaum's Series

67. Network Theory....... Prof Yoganarasimhan

68. Electronic Devices Circuits............Boylested and Neshelsky

69. Microelectronic Circuits............... Sedra and Smith

70. Electronic Devices Circuits............Millman and Halkias (Black Pad)

71. Microelectronics............Millman and Grabel

72. Integrated Electronics............Millman and Halkias

73. Electronic Circuits ....Schilling and Belove

74. Switching and Finite Automatic Theory ....Kohavi

75. Digital Logic and Computer Design ....Mano

76. Digital Electronics ....malvino and Leach

77. Digital Systems, Principles and Applications............Tocci

78. Microprocessor and its Applications ....Goankar

79. Microprocessors ....B Ram

80. Microprocessors ....Douglus V Hall

81. Automatic Control Systems ....BC Kuo

82. Control Systems ....Nagarath and Gopal

83. Modern Control Systems ....Ogata

84. OP Amps and Linear Integrated Circuits ....Gayakwad

85. Electrical and Electronic Measurements and Instrumentation............AK Sawhney

86. DC Machines Measurements and Measuring Instruments............GB Bharadhwajan

87. Electrical Machines ....Nagarath and Kohavi

88. Electrical Machines ....PS Bimhra

89. Electrical Technology ....Hughes

90. The performance and Design of AC Machines ....MG Say

91. Electrical Engg. (Problems and Solutions) ....Natesan

92. Electrical Machines ....Mukherjee & Chakravarthy

93. Electrical Machines ....JB Gupta

94. Elements of Power System Analysis ....William D Stevenson

95. Modern Power System Analysis ....Nagrath and Kothari

96. Electrical Power Systems ....Wadhwa

97. Power Systems ....VK Mehta

98. Power Systems ....Badri Ram

99. Power Electronics ....PS Bimbhra

100. Power Electronics ....Singh, Khanchandani

101. Power Electronics ....Rammoorthy

102. Electricity and Magnetism ....BS Agrawal

103. Engineering Physics (For Basic Electricity & Magnetism) ....Gaur and Gupta

104. Physics PART II (Electricity and Magnetism) ....Resnic and Hallday

105. Basic Electronics ....Millman and Grab

106. Engineering Electromagnetics ....William Hayt

107. Field Theory ....KA Gangadhar

108. Basic Electrical Engineering ....Nagarath and Kothari

109. Electricity and Magnetism ....Brijlal and Subramaniam

Made in the USA
Las Vegas, NV
01 April 2021

20508668R00069